How to...
eat the Weight Watchers way

Over 200 new recipes to help you make wise food choices

SIMON & SCHUSTER
A VIACOM COMPANY

Becky Johnson

First published in Great Britain by Simon & Schuster UK Ltd, 2005
A Viacom Company

Simon & Schuster UK Ltd, Africa House, 64–78 Kingsway, London WC2B 6AH

Weight Watchers Publications Team: Corrina Griffin, Lucy Davidson,
Kirsten Ware, Nina Bhogal

Photography by Steve Baxter
Styling by Liz Belton
Food preparation by Carol Tennant
Design by Jane Humphrey
Typesetting by Stylize Digital Artwork Ltd
Printed and bound in China

A CIP catalogue for this book is available from the British Library

ISBN 0743275993

Pictured on the back cover: Fabulous fish and bean stew page 27; Grilled Thai prawns with
salsa page 156; Chicken Kashmiri page 83; Lemon, strawberry and almond gâteau page 175

 POINTS™ **value logo**: You'll find this easy to read **POINTS** value logo on every recipe throughout this book. The logo represents the number of **POINTS** values per serving each recipe contains. The easy to use Full Choice food plan is designed to help you eat what you want, when you want – as long as you stay within your daily **POINTS** allowance – giving you the freedom to enjoy the food *you* love.

 You'll find this distinctive **NoCount**™ icon on every recipe that can be followed freely on the **NoCount** food plan. These recipes contain only foods that form part of the **NoCount** food plan.

This symbol denotes a vegetarian recipe and assumes that, where relevant, organic eggs, vegetarian cheese, vegetarian virtually fat free fromage frais and vegetarian low fat crème fraîche are used. Virtually fat free fromage frais and low fat crème fraîche may contain traces of gelatine so they are not always vegetarian. Please check the labels.

This symbol denotes a dish that can be frozen.

Recipe notes:
Egg size is medium, unless otherwise stated.

All fruits and vegetables medium sized unless otherwise stated.

Raw Eggs: Only the freshest eggs should be used. Pregnant women, the elderly and children should avoid recipes with eggs which are not fully cooked or raw.

Recipe timings are approximate and meant to be guidelines. Please note that the preparation time includes all the steps up to and following the main cooking time(s).

Contents

Healthy eating as a way of life

There is so much more to a healthy lifestyle than what you eat. It's about evaluating your cooking and eating habits – changing the essence of the way you eat, understanding the foods you choose to eat and finding a way to make this new, healthy way of eating natural to you.

This is the reason that we have chosen to call this cookbook *How to Eat the Weight Watchers Way*. Our hope is that through this cookbook, we will help you to discover a variety of healthy, delicious foods and recipes that you will love and delight in. It is so important that low fat cooking and eating should be an enjoyable and gratifying experience rather than a chore.

Often, learning to cook and eat healthily means going back to basics in the kitchen. Whether you are an experienced or novice cook, it's essential that you find the low fat, healthy foods that you and your family love and then learn to cook and eat them in a way that suits your everyday life. Habits are not always easy to change, and it may take some time to master new ones. For example, you may need to learn how to re-write your shopping lists or re-stock your storecupboard the Weight Watchers way. But, as you become used to your new lifestyle and find workable solutions that allow you to eat healthily without depriving you or your tastebuds, you'll find that this way becomes the better way of living.

How to Eat the Weight Watchers Way is a great stepping stone to a new, healthier lifestyle. It's not full of fancy, complicated recipes that take hours to perfect – it's about the essential, everyday foods and meals that we all enjoy. It's just the healthier version. It's a great kickstart into healthy eating, and is there to answer every normal eating occasion – from breakfasts and lunches to family eating and meals in minutes. This book recognises that people want to snack, eat sweet treats or sometimes need to cater for special occasions – so there are also recipes included for all of these requirements.

But, this book gives so much more than just the recipes themselves. It offers up hints and tips that make taking on the healthy eating habit so much easier. For example, you'll find essential low fat storecupboard ingredients, or instant fridge swaps that make pulling a healthy meal together so much easier; there's tips on how to cook or prepare meals in advance and how to manage your time in the kitchen more effectively. Plus, you'll find ways to portion control those foods that you find hard to resist, and information on why certain foods are good for you.

How to Eat the Weight Watchers Way is here to provide a sound, all round basic knowledge of healthy eating. Our hope is that throughout this book you will find your food 'saviours' and favourites – and will go on to experiment and explore these foods more thoroughly and make them your own – so that you can maintain a healthy weight, take on a new, better way of living and enjoy your life to the full.

The Weight Watchers **storecupboard**

You'll find below a handy list of all the most commonly used ingredients in this book. Once you've got your storecupboard stocked it will make eating the Weight Watchers way even easier.

Storecupboard list:

- [ ] Artificial sweetener, granulated
- [ ] Black beans, canned and dried
- [ ] Black pepper
- [ ] Balsamic vinegar
- [ ] Cannellini beans, canned and dried
- [ ] Chickpeas, canned and dried
- [ ] Chilli powder
- [ ] Cinnamon and nutmeg
- [ ] Coriander seeds
- [ ] Cornflour
- [ ] Couscous
- [ ] Cumin

- [ ] Curry powder
- [ ] Egg noodles
- [ ] Flour (plain and self raising)
- [ ] Fruit canned in natural juice (e.g. peaches, pineapple)
- [ ] Garam masala
- [ ] Garlic
- [ ] Ginger, fresh root
- [ ] Herbs, dried and fresh
- [ ] Honey, clear
- [ ] Kidney beans, canned and dried
- [ ] Lentils, canned and dried (brown, green or red)
- [ ] Long grain rice

- [ ] Low fat cooking spray
- [ ] Mustard seeds
- [ ] Mustard, wholegrain and English
- [ ] Olives
- [ ] Onion, red and white
- [ ] Pasta, dried (preferably wholemeal)
- [ ] Peas, frozen or canned
- [ ] Porridge oats
- [ ] Rice noodles
- [ ] Risotto rice
- [ ] Roasted red peppers, canned in brine
- [ ] Salt (low sodium or sea salt are best)
- [ ] Soy sauce
- [ ] Stock cubes
- [ ] Sugar free jelly
- [ ] Sweetcorn, frozen or canned
- [ ] Tomatoes, canned
- [ ] Tomato purée
- [ ] Tuna, canned in brine or springwater
- [ ] Vinegar, red and white wine
- [ ] Worcestershire sauce

Fresh Ingredients:

- [ ] 0% fat Greek yogurt
- [ ] Eggs
- [ ] Fruit and vegetables, fresh in season
- [ ] Low fat soft cheese
- [ ] Milk, skimmed or soya
- [ ] Polyunsaturated margarine
- [ ] Yogurt, low fat fruit and plain

Breakfasts and brunches

A wholesome breakfast is essential to healthy living and weight loss. Having breakfast will energise you, and inject vigour for the day ahead – ridding you of weariness and morning sluggishness. It gives your body the sustenance it needs to wake up and kickstart your metabolism. But, most importantly, it will give you control of your eating – helping to keep your hunger at bay, leaving you less tempted to reach for instant, fattening snacks mid-morning.

Healthy breakfasts don't have to be boring. In this chapter, all the basics are covered, offering you the choice of how best to start your day. You'll find it all, from an energising smoothie or zingy fresh juice, to a winter warming porridge or an English breakfast. It's all healthy, delicious and easy to prepare – ready to inject life into your morning.

(3½) Croque monsieur

3½ **POINTS** values per recipe   Serves 1

160 calories per serving

Takes 10 minutes

An adapted version of the usually very high fat French breakfast, this croque monsieur is a satisfying treat.

1 medium slice wholemeal bread
25 g (1 oz) low fat soft cheese with garlic and herbs
40 g (1½ oz) wafer thin ham
15 g (½ oz) half fat Cheddar cheese

● Heat the grill and toast one side of the bread.
● Spread the untoasted side of the bread with the soft cheese and then cover with the ham and sprinkle with the Cheddar cheese.
● Grill until golden and bubbling and eat immediately.

Top tip

For a vegetarian alternative replace the ham with a sliced tomato and 1 tablespoon of chutney. The **POINTS** values will remain the same.

Sort your surroundings...

For many of us cheese can be our downfall – if it's in the fridge we eat it! A great solution is to grate your cheddar into weighed out portions (e.g. 40 g/1½ oz) and then store these individual portioned bags in the freezer. When you want to use the cheese, simply take out a bag and let it thaw for about an hour before using.

(4) Full English breakfast

7½ **POINTS** values per recipe   Serves 2

240 calories per serving

Takes 20 minutes

This recipe shows you how easy it is to enjoy a full English breakfast while you are trying to lose weight.

100 g (3½ oz) turkey rashers
2 medium tomatoes, the riper the better, sliced in half crossways
2 slices wholemeal bread
low fat cooking spray
100 g (3½ oz) mushrooms, sliced
1 large lemon wedge
2 eggs
15 g (½ oz) low fat polyunsaturated margarine
salt and freshly ground black pepper

● Preheat the grill and place the turkey rashers and tomatoes, cut side up and seasoned, on the grill pan. Grill for 3–4 minutes then turn the turkey rashers over and grill again for 2 minutes, until golden and crispy.
● Meanwhile warm two serving plates, toast the bread and heat a non stick frying pan. Spray with the low fat cooking spray and then add the mushrooms. Stir fry for 3–4 minutes on a high heat, until softened then season and squeeze over the lemon and remove from the heat.
● Tip the mushrooms on to the serving plates and return the frying pan to a low heat. Spray again with the cooking spray and then carefully break in the two eggs and fry over a gentle heat until they are cooked how you like them.
● Meanwhile spread the toast with the margarine and slice in half, then place on the serving plates. Add the cooked turkey rashers, tomatoes and eggs and serve immediately.

Top tip

For a NoCount version of this breakfast, simply omit the toast and margarine.

(3) Eggs Florentine

5½ *POINTS* values per recipe   Serves 2

190 calories per serving

Takes 10 minutes

A classic brunch dish that's been adapted here for a healthier lifestyle.

175 g (6 oz) baby spinach leaves, washed
a pinch of fresh nutmeg
1 tablespoon vinegar (any type)
2 eggs
one muffin, sliced in half
2 tablespoons fat free fromage frais
2 pinches of paprika
salt and freshly ground black pepper

● Place the wet spinach in a saucepan with salt, pepper and the nutmeg. Cover and cook on a low heat, stirring occasionally, for 3–4 minutes until wilted.
● Heat a medium saucepan of water to a rolling boil and add the vinegar. One at a time, break the eggs into a cup and gently lower them from the cup into the boiling water. Poach the eggs for 2–3 minutes until the white is firm, but the yolk still runny (or how you prefer). Remove with a slotted spoon.
● Meanwhile toast the muffin and place on plates with a pile of the cooked spinach on each one. Make a slight hollow in the top of the spinach and carefully spoon in the poached eggs. Spoon the fromage frais over the eggs, dust with paprika to serve.

Sort your surroundings...

If bread is your downfall, an easy way to control what you eat is by freezing your sliced bread. When you are hungry, either pop a couple of frozen slices straight into the toaster (for slightly longer than from fresh) or allow the bread to thaw before eating.

(2½) Oaty pancakes with blueberries

9½ *POINTS* values per recipe   Serves 4

170 calories per serving

Takes 20 minutes

These delicious cinnamon flavoured fluffy pancakes make a very special breakfast or delectable dessert.

2 eggs, separated
50 g (1¾ oz) self raising flour
50 g (1¾ oz) porridge oats
1 tablespoon artificial sweetener plus a pinch
1 teaspoon ground cinnamon
150 ml (¼ pint) skimmed milk or soya milk
low fat cooking spray
150 g (5½ oz) fresh blueberries
1 tablespoon artificial sweetener

● Whisk the egg whites until stiff. In another large bowl beat together the egg yolks, flour, oats, the pinch of sweetener, cinnamon and milk.
● Fold the egg whites into the mixture with a large metal spoon being careful to keep as much of the volume as possible.
● Heat a non stick frying pan and spray with the low fat cooking spray. Place tablespoons of the batter in the frying pan to make little oval pancakes approximately 8 cm (3¼ inches) in diameter.
● Cook for 2–3 minutes until golden and spongy and then turn once, using a palette knife, or fish slice, and cook until golden on the other side.
● When cooked, place them on a plate and wrap in a tea towel. Keep warm while you cook the others (the mixture makes about 16 pancakes).
● Meanwhile warm the blueberries gently in a small saucepan with 100 ml (3½ fl oz) of water and the tablespoon of sweetener. Stir occasionally until the fruit has broken down.
● Serve the pancakes warm with the hot blueberry sauce, allowing four per person.

Bold berry smoothie

2½ POINTS values per recipe

195 calories per serving

Takes 5 minutes

Serves 1

Smoothies are a tasty way of helping towards the recommended five portions of fruit and vegetables in your diet every day.

1 small ripe banana
150 g (5½ oz) frozen mixed summer fruits
100 g (3½ oz) low fat plain yogurt

● Liquidise the ingredients, adding small quantities of water until you have the consistency you prefer, then drink immediately.

Top tips

As a dairy-free NoCount alternative use 100 g (3½ oz) Galia melon or Cantaloupe melon instead of the banana and yogurt. The **POINTS** values per serving will be 1.

Freeze the smoothie mixture in ice lolly moulds or ice cube trays for delicious, cooling summer treats.

Time saver...

Summer fruits are fantastic for smoothies and can be used from frozen. Simply store the berries in the freezer, and then add the frozen berries to the liquidiser with some low fat yogurt. It's an instant, ice-cold, tasty breakfast.

Smoked salmon and scrambled eggs

4 *POINTS* values per recipe Serves 1

270 calories per serving

Takes 5 minutes

A satisfying start to the day with a luxurious twist. Fresh chopped dill or parsley makes a delicious addition to this dish.

2 eggs, beaten
4 tablespoons skimmed milk or soya milk
50 g (1¾ oz) smoked salmon pieces, chopped if necessary
salt and freshly ground black pepper

● Place all the ingredients in a non stick saucepan and, using a wooden spoon, stir over a low heat until the eggs are just firm but not dry.

● Season to taste and serve immediately.

Top tip
You can usually buy smoked salmon offcuts quite cheaply in supermarkets and they are perfect for this recipe, which requires the salmon to be chopped into small pieces.

 ## Power porridge

4 *POINTS* values per recipe Serves 1

295 calories per serving Ⓨ

Takes 5 minutes

Porridge is quick and easy to make and will set you up for the whole morning. With the addition of some fresh fruit and calcium-rich milk, porridge is also one of the best nutritional breakfasts you can have.

40 g (1½ oz) porridge oats
100 ml (3½ fl oz) skimmed milk
1 small banana
50 g (1¾ oz) blueberries

● Place the porridge oats in a pan and add the 250 ml (9 fl oz) water. Bring to the boil and then simmer for 3–4 minutes, until thick and creamy.

● Serve in a bowl, top with the milk and fruit then eat while hot.

Top tip
You can vary the fruit: try it with fresh, sliced peaches, apricots, raspberries, strawberries, apples, pears, figs and/or blackberries.

Zingy vegetable juice

2½ POINTS values per recipe
Serves 1

275 calories per serving

Takes 5 minutes

This is a wonderful morning reviver packed with powerful nutrients and cleansing refreshment. For best results use a juicer, then you could use raw beetroot instead of cooked.

100 g (3½ oz) cooked beetroot (vacuum packed or freshly cooked and peeled), sliced
1 large carrot, sliced
4 cm (1½ inch) piece of fresh root ginger, peeled and grated finely
2 apples, peeled, cored and chopped roughly
150 g (5½ oz) red or white seedless grapes

● Place all the ingredients in a food processor or blender and blend for a few minutes or until fairly smooth. Strain and serve or serve it just as it is.

Food fantastic...

Grapes contain iron, potassium and fibre. They are powerful detoxifiers and can improve the condition of the skin and inhibit the formation of tumours. Purple grapes can be more effective than aspirin in reducing the risk of heart attacks..

Big fruit kickstart

3½ POINTS values per recipe
Serves 1

260 calories per serving

Takes 10 minutes

Claimed to be the optimum breakfast, fruit is easy to digest and consequently quick to give you energy. Bio yogurt, too, is great for our digestive systems. Try this breakfast for a few weeks and see how full of vitality you feel.

1 apple, cored and chopped
1 pear, cored and chopped
1 orange, peeled and sliced
2 plums, stoned and chopped
1 kiwi fruit, peeled and chopped
2 heaped tablespoons of low fat plain bio yogurt

● Toss all the fruit together in a bowl then spoon over the yogurt. Eat immediately.

Top tip

Vary the fruit, try to buy whatever is ripe and in season for the best flavour. Look for local produce as the less a fruit has travelled the fresher it should be – and it will have greater nutritional value. Huge bowls of pick-your-own raspberries and strawberries in the summer are wonderful.

Storecupboard laundry...

Replace highly processed breakfast cereals with wholegrain, unsweetened varieties, but best of all phase them out and make your own. Vary your breakfast with fruit, porridge, eggs, smoothies and so on.

Scrumptious soups

Tinned, packet or fresh, soups offer a fantastic instant solution to hunger pangs, comfort eating or over eating. And, once you have mastered how to make your own, they can become so much more: a meal, a starter or a satisfying snack, and they are also full of goodness.

This chapter explores how to make the most of the vast array of ingredients available in supermarkets – from the old classics (leek and potato), to seasonal soups (asparagus and fromage frais) to the more exotic (Jaipur dahl). As you experiment with your favourite ingredients, you can build up your own repertoire to suit your moods and seasonal favourites. Hot or cold, chunky or smooth – soups really are a versatile food that should be exploited.

All season minestrone (page 30)

(3) French onion soup

12½ **POINTS** values per recipe   Serves 4

230 calories per serving

Takes 15 minutes to prepare, 30 minutes to cook (without croûtons)

Treat yourself to this classic meal of a soup with its strong, satisfying flavour.

600 g (1 lb 5 oz) onions, peeled
low fat cooking spray
1 teaspoon caster sugar
1.5 litres (2¾ pints) hot vegetable stock
150 ml (¼ pint) dry white wine
8 x 2.5 cm (1 inch) slices French baguette, toasted on one side
50 g (1¾ oz) Emmenthal or mature Cheddar cheese, grated
salt and freshly ground black pepper

● Slice the onions very finely. Heat a large saucepan and spray with the low fat cooking spray then add the onions and sprinkle with the sugar. Sauté over a low heat for 20 minutes, scraping the bottom of the pan frequently with a wooden spoon, until the onions are golden and softened.

● Add the hot stock, seasoning and wine, bring to the boil then simmer, covered, for 15 minutes.

● Meanwhile preheat the grill to high. Place the bread, toasted side down, on a baking sheet and cover each slice with grated cheese. Grill for 2–3 minutes, until the cheese is bubbling and golden.

● Ladle the soup into warmed serving bowls and float the cheese croûtons on top. Grind black pepper over and serve.

Storecupboard basics...

Onions are an essential storecupboard ingredient and you should always try to keep a stock of them in your kitchen. They are a wonderful base to almost any dish – adding flavour and texture. Experiment to find your favourite – white onions, red onions, shallots, spring onions. Try roasting, sweating, frying – add to casseroles and stir fries or use them to make a delicious soup like in the recipe above.

(1) Thai spinach soup

3½ **POINTS** values per recipe   Serves 4

70 calories per serving

Takes 15 minutes

A super-quick and creamy soup which can be rustled up in 15 minutes. This soup can also be made with watercress instead of the spinach for the same **POINTS** values.

low fat cooking spray
2.5 cm (1 inch) piece of fresh root ginger, chopped finely
4 garlic cloves, crushed
1 teaspoon Thai curry paste
500 g (1 lb 2 oz) baby spinach or spinach, tough stems removed
    and leaves shredded,
1.2 litres (2 pints) vegetable stock
100 ml (3½ fl oz) reduced fat coconut milk
salt and freshly ground black pepper

● Heat a large saucepan and spray with the low fat cooking spray. Stir fry the ginger, garlic, and curry paste for a few minutes, until fragrant.

● Add the spinach and stock and bring to the boil. Simmer for a few moments and then liquidise the soup.

● Stir in the coconut milk and check the seasoning, then serve.

Top tip

Once you have added the coconut milk to the soup do not boil or the soup will split.

Summer vegetable soup

3 *POINTS* values per recipe — Serves 2

245 calories per serving — (omit the Worcestershire sauce) Ⓥ

Takes 20 minutes — (without croûtons) ❄

Rather like a gazpacho this is a raw, chilled soup packed with summer flavours – nutritional rocket fuel served with crunchy, garlicky croûtons.

For the croûtons
2 thick slices wholemeal bread, cubed
1 garlic clove, crushed
low fat cooking spray

For the soup
400 g (14 oz) ripe tomatoes, chopped roughly
1 courgette, chopped roughly
1/2 cucumber, chopped
1 medium red onion, chopped roughly, with some diced finely
    for garnish
1/2 red pepper, chopped roughly, with some diced finely for garnish
1 teaspoon balsamic vinegar
300 ml (1/2 pint) passata
1/4 teaspoon Tabasco sauce
1 tablespoon Worcestershire sauce
1 tablespoon soy sauce
a large bunch of basil, chopped roughly, but the small leaves kept
    whole for garnish
salt and freshly ground black pepper

● For the croûtons, preheat the oven to Gas Mark 4/180°C/fan oven 160°C. On a baking tray toss the bread cubes with the garlic and seasoning and then spray with the low fat cooking spray. Bake for 15–20 minutes, shaking the tray occasionally and keeping a close eye on the croûtons, until they are golden brown and crisp.
● Meanwhile place all the soup ingredients, less those for the garnish, in a liquidiser and blend until smooth, adding a little cold water if too thick. Tip into bowls (or chill in the fridge first) and serve scattered with the remaining finely diced red onion, red pepper, small basil leaves and the croûtons.

Beetroot and crème fraîche soup

9 1/2 *POINTS* values per recipe — Serves 4

235 calories per serving — Ⓥ

Takes 30 minutes — ❄

This luxurious soup is simplicity itself to make but impressive enough to serve to guests for a celebratory meal.

low fat cooking spray
4 shallots or 2 onions, peeled and chopped
2 medium sized potatoes, each weighing about 100g (3 1/2 oz),
    peeled and chopped
1 kg (2 lb 4 oz) vacuum packed cooked beetroot, drained and
    chopped
1.2 litres (2 pints) vegetable stock
150 g (5 1/2 oz) reduced fat crème fraîche
salt and freshly ground black pepper
a small bunch of chives, chopped, to garnish (optional)

● Heat a large pan and spray with the low fat cooking spray. Stir fry the shallots or onions and potatoes for 5 minutes, until golden, adding a little water, if they start to stick.
● Add the beetroot and stock and stir together, then cover and bring to the boil. Simmer gently for 15 minutes and then liquidise and return to the pan, but do not reheat.
● Check the seasoning and then add the crème fraîche and swirl together rather than mixing it in fully. Serve garnished with chives, if using.

Top tip
If reheating this soup be careful not to boil as it may split.

Parsnip, ham and apple soup

8½ *POINTS* values per recipe   Serves 2

315 calories per serving

Takes 15 minutes to prepare, 45 minutes to cook

The addition of apple gives this soup a sweet edge that enhances the intense, soothing parsnip flavour.

low fat cooking spray
1 large onion, chopped roughly
500 g (1lb 2 oz) parsnips, tops removed and chopped roughly
1 cooking apple, peeled and cored, chopped roughly
1.5 litres (2¾ pints) vegetable stock
150 ml (¼ pint) skimmed milk or soya milk
100 g (3½ oz) lean ham, chopped
salt and freshly ground black pepper

● Spray a large saucepan with the low fat cooking spray and then stir fry the onion for 3 minutes, until softened and golden, adding a little water if necessary to stop it from sticking.

● Add the parsnips and apple and cover with the vegetable stock. Bring to the boil and then simmer for 45 minutes, covered.

● Liquidise and then stir in the milk. Add the chopped ham and allow to heat it through. Check the seasoning and serve.

Asparagus and fromage frais soup

2 *POINTS* values per recipe   Serves 4

65 calories per serving

Takes 20 minutes

A silky, delicately flavoured spring soup.

low fat cooking spray
2 garlic cloves, sliced finely
1 large onion, chopped roughly
500 g (1 lb 2 oz) asparagus, woody stems cut off, chopped roughly
1.2 litres (2 pints) vegetable stock
100 g (3½ oz) virtually fat free fromage frais
salt and freshly ground black pepper
a small bunch of chervil, torn into pieces, to garnish (optional)

● Heat a large saucepan and spray with the low fat cooking spray then stir fry the garlic and onion for a few minutes, until softened and golden, adding a few tablespoons of water, if necessary, to stop them sticking.

● Add the asparagus and stock and bring to the boil. Simmer for 5–10 minutes and then liquidise. Return to the pan and stir in the fromage frais and seasoning. Serve scattered with the chervil if using.

Time saver...

Make soups into an instant snack or lunch by preparing them in advance and freezing. Make a large batch by multiplying up the recipe quantities. Then, measure the soup out into portions and freeze. When you are ready to eat, simply take it out of the freezer and pop in the microwave or gently thaw on the hob – for a quick, wholesome and satisfying filler.

Fabulous fish and bean soup

12½ *POINTS* values per recipe   Serves 4

215 calories per serving

Takes 40 minutes

A fabulously filling and tasty meal of a soup that needs no accompaniments.

low fat cooking spray
1 large onion, chopped finely
4 garlic cloves, crushed
a bay leaf
a pinch of saffron, soaked in 2 tablespoons boiling water
   (optional)
3 stalks celery, sliced finely
400 g can of chopped tomatoes
400 g can of red kidney beans, drained and rinsed
zest of a lemon, grated finely
1 tablespoon fennel seeds
1 tablespoon tomato purée
1.2 litres (2 pints) fish or vegetable stock
500 g (1 lb 2 oz) cod, fresh, or frozen and defrosted, skinned
   and cubed
a small bunch of parsley, chopped
salt and freshly ground black pepper

● Heat a large non stick saucepan, spray with the low fat cooking spray and stir fry the onion and garlic for 5 minutes, until softened, adding a little water to stop them sticking.

● Add the bay leaf, saffron (if using) and soaking water, celery, tomatoes, beans, lemon zest, fennel seeds, tomato purée and stock and bring to the boil. Cover and simmer for 20 minutes.

● Add the fish to the pan and cook for 7–10 minutes until just cooked through. Check the seasoning, then scatter with chopped parsley and serve.

Summer pea, ham and mint soup

8½ *POINTS* values per recipe   Serves 2

235 calories per serving

Takes 15 minutes

A very quick, simple and fresh tasting soup.

low fat cooking spray
1 onion, peeled and sliced thinly
500 g (1 lb 2 oz) peas, freshly podded or frozen
600 ml (1 pint) vegetable stock
a bunch of fresh mint, chopped
100 g (3½ oz) lean ham, chopped into small pieces
salt and freshly ground black pepper

● Spray a large non stick saucepan with the low fat cooking spray and stir fry the onion for 5 minutes, until softened, adding a little water if it sticks.

● Add the peas, stock, seasoning and half the mint. Bring to the boil and then simmer for 5 minutes. Add the rest of the mint, but reserve a little for garnishing.

● Liquidise the soup in batches and return to the pan. Add the ham and warm through, check the seasoning and then serve garnished with the reserved mint and more black pepper.

Storecupboard basics...

Stock is an indispensable ingredient when eating the Weight Watchers way. You should always keep a good supply – either buy stock cubes from the supermarket or make your own. You'll find that stock is often used in this cookbook as a base for many dishes, such as soups, casseroles or curries.

0 POINTS Roast butternut squash soup

0 POINTS values per recipe — Serves 4

165 calories per serving

Takes 15 minutes to prepare, 45 minutes to cook

Roasting the butternut squash for this soup gives it a fuller flavour and a thick, rich texture.

1.5 kg (3 lb 5 oz) butternut squash or pumpkin, peeled, de-seeded and cut into chunks
low fat cooking spray
2 onions, sliced into thin wedges
1 teaspoon ground cinnamon
1/2 teaspoon ground cloves
2.5 cm (1 inch) piece of fresh root ginger, chopped roughly
1.2 litres (2 pints) vegetable stock
salt and freshly ground black pepper
a small bunch of parsley, chopped, to garnish (optional)

● Preheat the oven to Gas Mark 6/200°C/fan oven 180°C, place the butternut squash or pumpkin in a baking tray and roast for 30 minutes until tender.
● 10 minutes before the pumpkin or squash is ready, heat a large saucepan and spray with the low fat cooking spray. Stir fry the onions with the spices and ginger until softened, adding a little water to prevent them sticking.
● Add the roast squash and stock. Stir and bring to the boil and then turn down the heat and simmer for 5 minutes.
● Liquidise the soup in batches and then pour back into a pan. Season and heat through. Serve sprinkled with parsley, if using.

1½ POINTS Sweet potato and chilli soup

6 POINTS values per recipe — Serves 4

175 calories per serving

Takes 30 minutes

This silky sweet and hot soup is just the thing for a cold wintry day.

low fat cooking spray
2 large onions, peeled and chopped, roughly
2 garlic cloves, crushed
1–2 small red chillies, de-seeded and chopped roughly
500 g (1 lb 2 oz) sweet potatoes, peeled and chopped roughly
500 g (1 lb 2 oz) carrots, peeled and chopped roughly
1.2 litres (2 pints) vegetable stock
salt and freshly ground black pepper

● Spray a large saucepan with the low fat cooking spray and then stir fry the onions and garlic until soft and golden, adding a little water if necessary to stop them sticking.
● Stir in the chillies and then add the sweet potatoes and carrots. Cover all the ingredients with stock. Cover the pan and bring to the boil then simmer for 20 minutes, or until the vegetables are tender.
● Liquidise the soup and return to the pan. Season and adjust the consistency to your taste by adding a little water, if necessary.

Courgette and coriander soup

0 POINTS values per recipe

Serves 2

90 calories per serving

Takes 15 minutes to prepare, 15 minutes to cook

A lovely fresh-flavoured and bright green summery soup.

low fat cooking spray
1/2 teaspoon ground coriander seeds
1 garlic clove, crushed
1 large onion, peeled and sliced thinly
500 g (1 lb 2 oz) courgettes, peeled and chopped roughly
600 ml (1 pint) vegetable stock
a bunch of fresh coriander, including roots if possible, washed and chopped
salt and freshly ground black pepper

● Spray a large non stick saucepan with the low fat cooking spray and stir fry the coriander seeds, garlic and onion for 5 minutes, until softened, adding a little water if they stick.

● Add the courgettes, stock, seasoning and the chopped stems and roots of the coriander. Bring to the boil and then simmer for 5 minutes, until the courgettes are tender. Add the coriander leaves, but reserve a little for garnishing.

● Liquidise the soup and return to the pan. Warm through, check the seasoning and then serve garnished with the reserved coriander leaves.

All season minestrone

2 POINTS values per recipe

Serves 4

205 calories per serving

Takes 15 minutes to prepare, 30 minutes to cook

This hearty soup is easy to prepare and is a meal in itself.

low fat cooking spray
2 leeks or 1 large onion, chopped finely
100 g (7 oz) potatoes, peeled and diced
1.5 litres (2¾ pints) hot vegetable stock
100 g (3½ oz) small dried pasta shapes or broken up spaghetti
1 teaspoon dried Mediterranean herbs
400 g can of chopped tomatoes
4 medium carrots peeled and diced
200 g (7 oz) green beans, sliced
1 bunch flatleaf parsley or basil, chopped (optional)
salt and freshly ground black pepper

● Heat a large saucepan then spray with the low fat cooking spray. Add the leeks or onion and stir fry for 5 minutes, adding a little water, if they stick, until soft and golden.

● Add the potatoes, stock, pasta, dried herbs, tomatoes and carrots and bring to the boil. Turn down the heat, cover and cook for 15 minutes. Then remove the lid and add the beans for a further 5 minutes.

● Taste and season, then stir in the chopped fresh herbs, if using and serve with a grinding of black pepper on each portion.

Roast tomato and garlic soup

0 *POINTS* values per recipe

70 calories per serving

Takes 1 hour

Serves 2

(omit the Worcestershire sauce) Ⓥ

❄

An intensely flavoured soup that's thick, rich and satisfying.

500 g (1 lb 2 oz) ripe tomatoes, quartered
2 red onions, peeled and cut into wedges
1 bulb of garlic, divided into cloves but unpeeled
1 red pepper, de-seeded and quartered
low fat cooking spray
300 ml (1/2 pint) hot vegetable stock
1 tablespoon balsamic vinegar
1 tablespoon Worcestershire sauce
salt and freshly ground black pepper
a small bunch of fresh parsley, chopped roughly, to garnish
   (optional)

● Preheat the oven to Gas Mark 7/220°C/fan oven 200°C and put the tomatoes, onions, garlic and red pepper into a large roasting tin. Season and spray with the low fat cooking spray. Roast for 45 minutes, until the vegetables begin to char at the edges.
● Remove the vegetables from the oven and allow to cool for a few minutes; then squeeze the garlic cloves out of their skins and purée in a food processor with all the other roasted vegetables, stock, vinegar and Worcestershire sauce.
● Tip the purée into a saucepan and heat through for a few minutes. Season and serve scattered with the parsley, if using.

Leek and potato soup

5½ *POINTS* values per recipe

175 calories per serving

Takes 40 minutes

Serves 4

Ⓥ

❄

A perfect winter soup; smooth, subtle, substantial and comforting. It is simple and quick to make and full of goodness.

low fat cooking spray
400 g (14 oz) potatoes, peeled and chopped into small pieces
6 large leeks, split in half, washed and chopped finely
1.2 litres (2 pints) vegetable stock
300 ml (1/2 pint) skimmed milk
a pinch of nutmeg
salt and freshly ground black pepper
a bunch of chives, snipped, to garnish (optional)

● Heat a large saucepan and spray with the low fat cooking spray. Add the potatoes and stir fry for a few minutes. Add the leeks, stir together and add the stock.
● Bring to the boil and then simmer, covered, for 20 minutes, until the leeks and potatoes are tender.
● Add the milk, nutmeg and seasoning and stir through. Serve hot, garnished with snipped chives, if using, and black pepper.

Food fantastic...

Potatoes are a great source of vitamin C, which helps your body to absorb iron and also produce collagen – important for skin and bone structure.

Lentil, porcini and bacon soup

5 POINTS VALUE

21 *POINTS* values per recipe   Serves 4

255 calories per serving

Takes 35 minutes

Porcini is the Italian word for cep mushrooms usually sold sliced and dried. Any dried mushrooms will do as they impart a lovely strong, earthy flavour to this thick and comforting soup.

low fat cooking spray
1 large onion, chopped finely
200 g (7 oz) (8 rashers) thickly sliced lean back bacon, all fat
    removed, sliced into small pieces
2 celery sticks, chopped finely
200 g (7 oz) dried red or brown lentils
1.2 litres (2 pints) vegetable stock
15 g (¹/₂ oz) porcini, chopped finely
a small bunch of fresh thyme or tarragon, tough stems removed,
    chopped (optional)
salt and freshly ground black pepper

● Spray a large non stick saucepan with the low fat cooking spray and stir fry the onion with the bacon and celery until golden and softened, adding a little water if they stick.

● Add the lentils, stock, porcini and thyme or tarragon, if using, reserving a few sprigs, and bring to the boil. Turn down the heat and simmer for 20 minutes, until the lentils are tender.

● Check the seasoning and serve the soup garnished with the reserved tarragon or thyme, if using.

Food fantastic...

Lentils offer a great source of protein, and are rich in fibre and complex carbohydrates, making them very filling. And, the good news is that just 3 heaped tablespoons count as 1 portion of your fruit and veg for the day.

Jaipur-style dahl soup

¹/₂ POINTS VALUE

3 *POINTS* values per recipe   Serves 4

215 calories per serving

Takes 30 minutes

Dahl is an Indian lentil dish which has many different regional versions. This soup keeps very well, covered, in the fridge, for up to 3 days. Serve with spoons of 0% fat plain yogurt.

low fat cooking spray
3 garlic cloves, sliced finely
2 tablespoons cumin seeds
¹/₂ teaspoon fennel seeds
2.5 cm (1 inch) piece of fresh ginger, peeled and chopped
1–2 green chillies, de-seeded and chopped finely (optional)
1.2 litres (2 pints) vegetable stock
¹/₂ teaspoon ground turmeric
200 g (7 oz) red lentils, drained and rinsed
2 large carrots, diced finely
¹/₂ cauliflower, cut into small florets
juice of half a lemon
a small bunch of fresh coriander, chopped
salt and freshly ground black pepper

● Heat a large saucepan and spray with the low fat cooking spray and then stir fry the garlic until golden. Add the cumin, fennel, ginger and chillies and stir fry for a further few minutes until they become fragrant.

● Add the stock, turmeric and lentils and stir together. Bring to the boil removing any scum that collects on the top, and then add the vegetables. Cover and simmer for 15 minutes and then add the lemon juice and coriander. Check the seasoning and serve.

Vibrant veggies

Vegetables are good for us. We all know it – so why is it so difficult to eat five portions throughout the day? The simple answer is that a pile of carrots served on the side of your plate can be uninspiring, and so we just don't want to eat them! The trick with vegetables is in finding ways to make the most out of the variety available to us, and then to do something interesting with them to really maximise their flavour.

This chapter is all about experimenting with vegetables in a simple, effective and tasty way to make interesting, mouthwatering meals and snacks. From aubergine crisps to spicy parsnip and leek patties, these recipes combine flavours and textures that really accentuate and emphasise the vegetables used.

Roasted stuffed mushrooms (page 42)

Soufflé baked potatoes

11½ *POINTS* values per recipe

380 calories per serving

Takes 15 minutes to prepare, 1 hour 15 minutes to cook

Serves 2 Ⓨ

Simple baked potatoes take on an exciting new character with a light cheese and onion filling. Serve these with a crisp salad.

2 large (approx 300 g/10½ oz each) baking potatoes
low fat cooking spray
1 small bunch of spring onions, sliced finely
4 tablespoons skimmed milk
50 g (1¾ oz) cherry tomatoes, quartered
1 egg white
50 g (1¾ oz) half fat Cheddar cheese, grated
salt and freshly ground black pepper

● Preheat the oven to Gas Mark 5/190°C/fan oven 170°C. Prick the potatoes all over with a fork and bake for 1 hour, or until soft.
● Meanwhile spray a frying pan with the low fat cooking spray and stir fry the spring onions until just tender and golden.
● Cut the potatoes in half and scoop out the flesh into a large bowl. Add the milk and mash together until you have a smooth blend.
● Stir in the fried spring onions and the tomatoes and season. Whisk the egg white until stiff and fluffy and then fold carefully into the potato mixture with the grated cheese.
● Place the potato skins on a baking tray and refill them with the potato mixture, piling up high. Bake for 10–15 minutes, until golden and hot. Serve immediately.

 ## Mediterranean pasta salad

20 *POINTS* values per recipe

355 calories per serving

Takes 25 minutes

Serves 4 Ⓨ

This is an ideal recipe for a griddle pan. Otherwise grill the vegetables in batches under the grill or bake them in a hot oven.

240 g (8½ oz) penne or other pasta shapes
2 red onions, peeled and cut into thin wedges
4 courgettes, cut lengthways into long strips
2 red peppers, de-seeded and sliced
2 aubergines, sliced lengthways into long thin pieces
low fat cooking spray
100 g (3½ oz) feta cheese
a bunch of mint, chopped
2 garlic cloves, crushed
2 tablespoons balsamic vinegar
salt and freshly ground black pepper

● Cook the pasta according to the pack instructions in plenty of boiling, salted water, and then drain.
● Lay the vegetables in one layer on the grill pan and sprinkle with salt and freshly ground black pepper. Spray with the low fat cooking spray and grill for 4–5 minutes until they are golden and beginning to crisp. You may have to grill the vegetables in several batches depending on the size of your grill pan. Place them in a large bowl.
● Add the cooked pasta, feta, mint, garlic and balsamic vinegar to the bowl, check the seasoning, toss together and serve.

Storecupboard basics...

Herbs are always good to have to hand. You can add so much flavour, without any fat, by simply adding a sprinkling of herbs to your dishes. Experiment until you find your favourite varieties, and then always try to keep some stashed! You can buy dried or fresh herbs from all the supermarkets – and if you are really ambitious you can even try growing your own.

(0 POINTS VALUE) Green beans with rosemary

1 *POINT* values per recipe   Serves 4

45 calories per serving

Takes 10 minutes

(3 POINTS VALUE) Veggie burgers

12 *POINTS* values per recipe   Serves 4

300 calories per serving

Takes 20 minutes to prepare, 20 minutes to cook

A great example of the Italian cucina povera – the use of inexpensive ingredients in the simplest ways – with delicious results.

500 g (1 lb 2 oz) green beans, topped

1 teaspoon olive or walnut or hazelnut oil

a few sprigs of rosemary, chopped, leave a few whole sprigs for garnishing

2 garlic cloves, sliced finely

1½ teaspoons red or white wine vinegar

salt and freshly ground black pepper

● Bring a saucepan of lightly salted water to the boil and blanch the beans for 4–5 minutes, until they are al dente and still bright green. Drain them and run under cold water to refresh.

● Toss the beans with the other ingredients and serve or allow to marinate for 10–15 minutes. Serve garnished with a few sprigs of rosemary.

These soft golden patties are full of vegetables and firm tofu. They are quick and easy to make, very low in fat and popular with kids. Serve in sesame seed baps with salad but don't forget to count the *POINTS* values.

400 g (14 oz) potatoes, peeled and quartered

250 g (9 oz) frozen mixed vegetables, e.g. sweetcorn, beans, peppers

low fat cooking spray

2 leeks, chopped roughly

1 garlic clove, crushed

250 g pack of firm tofu, crumbled

100 g (3½ oz) fresh breadcrumbs

2 tablespoons soy sauce

1 tablespoon tomato purée

a small bunch of fresh parsley or coriander (optional)

salt and freshly ground black pepper

● Cook the potatoes in lightly salted, boiling water for 15 minutes, until tender. Drain well. Cook the frozen vegetables in boiling, salted water for 5 minutes, until tender. Drain well.

● Meanwhile heat a non stick frying pan, spray with the low fat cooking spray and fry the leeks and garlic. Mash the potatoes and then add the cooked frozen vegetables and all the other ingredients including the cooked leeks and garlic. Mix together well and then shape the mixture into eight burgers.

● Heat the frying pan and spray with low fat cooking spray. Fry the burgers for 4–5 minutes on each side until golden brown and cooked through.

Time saver...

When you buy fresh herbs, you can preserve them by setting the sprigs into ice cubes and storing in the freezer. Then, when you need a quick addition of flavour, simply drop a couple of cubes into your cooking pot.

Braised red cabbage

1½ *POINTS* values per recipe   Serves 4

35 calories per serving

Takes 50 minutes

This slightly sweet and sour cabbage is cooked until it is meltingly soft and delicious. Try it with the Roast pork chops page 109.

1 red cabbage, quartered and shredded finely
1 tablespoon white wine vinegar
2 dessert apples, peeled, cored and grated
salt and freshly ground black pepper

● Put all the ingredients in a large saucepan with 100 ml (3½ fl oz) water. Cover and bring to the boil and then simmer on a low heat for 45 minutes or until the cabbage is meltingly soft and the liquid has almost gone. Season and serve.

Top tip
This dish keeps well in the fridge for up to three days, and actually improves in flavour.

Food fantastic...

Cabbage contains the mineral magnesium, which helps your body to use energy and your muscles to function effectively.

Phytochemicals such as anthocyanins found in the red/purple pigments of fruit and vegetables especially red cabbage, are among the most potent antioxidants. They, therefore, protect against disease and help you stay younger looking!

French style braised peas and carrots

2½ *POINTS* values per recipe

50 calories per serving

Takes 20 minutes

Serves 4

A tasty, country style French dish that makes the perfect accompaniment to grilled or roast meat or fish.

low fat cooking spray
a small bunch of spring onions, sliced finely
200 g (7 oz) baby carrots, washed, and larger ones sliced
200 ml (7 fl oz) vegetable stock
200 g (7 oz) frozen petit pois
1 Romaine lettuce, shredded
salt and freshly ground black pepper

● Spray a large saucepan with the low fat cooking spray and fry the spring onions for a few minutes, until softened, adding a little water if they stick. Add the carrots and stock and stir.

● Bring to the boil and then simmer for 5 minutes before adding the petit pois and the lettuce. Cover the pan. Return to the boil for a further 4 minutes. Season and serve.

Storecupboard basics...

Always keep some pepper in the cupboard as it adds a final, distinctive flavour to your dishes. You can buy pepper whole, cracked, or ground – but try to buy whole peppercorns and then pop in a pepper mill, for freshly ground pepper at the last minute. Freshly ground pepper is more pungent then pre-ground and can be stored for up to a year.

Roasted roots

½ *POINTS* values per recipe

145 calories per serving

Takes 15 minutes to prepare, 1 hour to cook

Serves 4

Warm, crispy and caramelised veggies with a simple caper and mustard dressing. This can also be served as an accompaniment to roast meats like the Easter Sunday roast lamb on page 150.

½ pumpkin or butternut squash, peeled, de-seeded and cut into
*   even sized chunks*
1 medium turnip, cut into even sized chunks
1 medium swede, cut into even sized chunks
4 red onions cut into even sized wedges
1 celeriac, peeled and cut into even sized chunks
4 carrots, peeled and cut into even sized chunks
a small bunch of fresh rosemary or thyme, leaves removed from
*   stems and chopped*
low fat cooking spray
salt and freshly ground black pepper
For the dressing
1 tablespoon capers, drained and rinsed
1 tablespoon Dijon mustard
1 tablespoon balsamic vinegar
2 tablespoons virtually fat free fromage frais
2 tablespoons cold water

● Preheat the oven to Gas Mark 7/220°C/fan oven 200°C. Place all the vegetables and the rosemary or thyme in a large roasting tray, season and spray them several times with the low fat cooking spray.

● Roast for 45 minutes – 1 hour or until the vegetables are golden and tender, stirring them around every now and then during cooking.

● Meanwhile make the dressing by mixing the ingredients together in a small bowl. When the vegetables are cooked, heap them on to serving plates and spoon over the dressing to serve.

Roasted stuffed mushrooms

2½ *POINTS* values per recipe   Serves 2

145 calories per serving

Takes 40 minutes

A quick and delicious main course accompanied by fresh steamed vegetables or a vegetable stir fry.

low fat cooking spray

4 large mushrooms e.g. Portobello or large field or chestnut mushrooms, stems removed & chopped

1 onion, chopped finely

1 garlic clove, crushed

zest of 1 lemon

a small bunch of fresh thyme, leaves removed from stems and chopped

2 courgettes, diced

100 g (3½ oz) baby spinach

2 tablespoons soy sauce

100 g (3½ oz) low fat soft cheese with onion and chives

50 ml (2 fl oz) vegetable stock

● Preheat the oven to Gas Mark 4/180°C/fan oven 160°C and spray a baking tray with the low fat cooking spray. Place the mushrooms, open side up, on the tray.

● Spray a large frying pan with the low fat cooking spray and fry the onion and garlic for a few minutes, until softened, adding a little water if necessary to stop them sticking.

● Add the lemon zest, thyme, courgettes, spinach, mushroom stems and soy sauce and stir fry for a couple of minutes. Remove from the heat and add the low fat soft cheese, allow it to melt and then stir through the vegetables.

● Pile this mixture into the mushrooms, add the stock to the tray and roast for 15 minutes, until the filling is golden and the mushrooms are tender.

 Roasted vegetables with yogurt sauce

4 *POINTS* values per recipe   Serves 4

220 calories per serving

Takes 30 minutes to prepare, 1 hour to cook

These winter vegetables roasted until crisp and golden make a simple but satisfying mid week supper dish.

4 red onions, cut into wedges

2 garlic bulbs, broken into cloves but left unpeeled

4 parsnips, peeled and cut into 6–8 long wedges lengthways

4 carrots, peeled and cut into 6–8 long wedges lengthways

2 beetroots, cut into 6–8 wedges

low fat cooking spray

250 ml (9 fl oz) vegetable stock

a bunch of fresh coriander, chopped roughly

For the yogurt sauce

250 g (9 oz) low fat plain yogurt

2 teaspoons cumin seeds

1 garlic clove, crushed

2 spring onions, chopped finely

salt and freshly ground black pepper

● Preheat the oven to Gas Mark 6/200°C/fan oven 180°C. Place all the vegetables in a large roasting tray and spray them a few times with the low fat cooking spray. Roast for 30 minutes.

● Pour in half the stock. Season and roast for another 30 minutes. Meanwhile make the yogurt sauce by mixing all the ingredients together in a small bowl.

● Remove the cooked vegetables from the oven, place them in a large serving bowl and sprinkle with the coriander.

● Place the roasting tin on the hob and heat until the juices are bubbling. Add the rest of the stock and allow to bubble, on a high heat, until you have a syrupy sauce. Pour this over the vegetables and serve with the yogurt sauce.

Creamy penne with peas

35 *POINTS* values per recipe   Serves 6

385 calories per serving

Takes 25 minutes

A very quick and summery pasta that could be made with whatever fresh vegetables or salad leaves you have available.

450 g (1 lb) penne pasta
450 g (1 lb) shelled fresh peas or frozen petit pois
low fat cooking spray
a bunch of spring onions, sliced finely
2 garlic cloves, sliced finely
300 g (10½ oz) low fat soft cheese with garlic and herbs
100 g (3½ oz) rocket or other salad leaf
zest and juice of 1 lemon
salt and freshly ground black pepper

● Cook the pasta according to the pack instructions in a saucepan of boiling salted water and 2 minutes before it is ready add the peas to the pan. Drain both together and place back in the pan.
● Meanwhile heat a non stick frying pan and spray with the low fat cooking spray. Stir fry the spring onions and garlic for two minutes.
● Add the fried onions and garlic, soft cheese, and rocket to the hot pasta and fold in with plenty of black pepper and the lemon zest and juice. Check the seasoning and serve.

Storecupboard basics...

Low fat cooking spray, such as Fry Light, is an absolute must for eating the Weight Watchers way. It works as a substitute for oil, but only has one calorie per spray. You can use it for frying, roasting, browning and grilling. You can get different varieties, with either sunflower or olive oil bases, depending on your preference.

Spicy parsnip and leek patties

10 *POINTS* values per recipe   Serves 4

180 calories per serving

Takes 15 minutes to prepare, 30 minutes to cook

Parsnips and leeks are plentiful and flavoursome through our wintry months. These versatile patties can be eaten as a veggie meal or as an accompaniment to a curry or grilled meat or fish. They can also be made bite-sized and served warm or cold at a party.

1 kg (2 lb 4 oz) parsnips, peeled and cut into chunks
low fat cooking spray
2 garlic cloves, crushed
1 teaspoon cumin seeds
1 teaspoon garam masala
1 teaspoon ground turmeric
1 large leek, sliced finely
a small bunch of coriander, chopped
salt and freshly ground black pepper

● Place the parsnips in a saucepan of boiling water and simmer for 15 minutes, until tender. Drain and mash them.
● Meanwhile heat a non stick frying pan and spray with the low fat cooking spray. Add the garlic and spices and stir fry until the cumin seeds begin to pop and the spices become fragrant. Add the leek and a few tablespoons of water then stir fry for a further 5 minutes, until the leek is soft.
● Stir the leek mixture into the mashed parsnips with the seasoning and the coriander. Allow the mixture to cool enough to be able to handle it. Preheat the oven to Gas Mark 6/200°C/fan oven 180°C.
● Using your hands shape the mixture into 12 patties. Place them on a baking tray that has been sprayed with low fat cooking spray. Bake the patties for 15 minutes, until golden brown.

⓪ Leeks à la niçoise

0 *POINTS* values per recipe — Serves 2

165 calories per serving

Takes 25 minutes

Great as an accompaniment to hot dishes such as Roast pork chops with apple stuffing (page 109) or, in the summer, serve it with dishes such as Courgettes with mint (page 46) or Warm broad beans and smoked ham pittas (page 112).

low fat cooking spray
1 kg (2 lb 4 oz) leeks, sliced into rounds
a small bunch of thyme, tough stems removed, tender stems and leaves chopped, or 1 teaspoon dried thyme
400 g can of chopped tomatoes
3 garlic cloves, crushed
1 tablespoon balsamic vinegar
1 tablespoon red wine vinegar
1 tablespoon tomato purée

● Heat a large saucepan and spray with the low fat cooking spray. Stir fry the leeks for 5 minutes or so, until they are translucent.
● Add all the other ingredients and then cover and simmer for 20 minutes or so, until the leeks are tender, adding a little water if necessary to keep the leeks moist. The time will depend on how young the leeks are.

Storecupboard basics...

Balsamic vinegar is a great option if you are eating healthily, as it is a rich, sweet and fragrant vinegar that adds a wonderful flavour to food, without adding any fat. Drizzle balsamic vinegar over cooked vegetables, meat or for something surprising toss a few drops of balsamic vinegar in with sliced strawberries for a refreshing treat.

④ Potato wedges with chilli dip

8 *POINTS* values per recipe — Serves 2

335 calories per serving

Takes 15 minutes to prepare, 35 minutes to cook — (chilli dip) ❄

The crispy crust on these potatoes will give you all the satisfaction of a plate of chips without the fat.

2 large baking potatoes (weighing approx 300 g/10½ oz), chopped into wedges
2 teaspoons dried oregano or herbes de Provence
2 garlic cloves, crushed
salt and freshly ground black pepper
For the chilli dip
low fat cooking spray
a bunch of spring onions, chopped finely
1 garlic clove, crushed
200 g can of chopped tomatoes
1 red chilli, de-seeded and chopped finely
1 tablespoon balsamic vinegar
a small bunch of fresh basil or coriander, chopped

● First parboil the potatoes. Place them in a large saucepan of cold water and bring them to the boil. Simmer for 10–15 minutes, until just tender. Preheat the oven to Gas Mark 6/200°C/fan oven 180°C.
● Make the chilli dip by heating a medium saucepan and spraying it with the low fat cooking spray. Stir fry the spring onions and garlic for a few minutes, until softened and then add the other ingredients.
● Bring to the boil and simmer gently for 10 minutes until reduced and thickened, season and pour into a serving bowl.
● Meanwhile drain the potatoes and place them in a roasting tin. Spray them with the low fat cooking spray, season, and scatter with the herbs and garlic. Toss it all together. Roast for 20 minutes turning occasionally, until golden and crisp and cooked through. Serve hot with the chilli dip.

Warm broccoli salad with mustard dressing

1 POINTS values per recipe

170 calories per serving

Takes 10 minutes

Serves 2

Ⓨ

A light and virtuous lunch or supper dish with satisfyingly strong flavours. Try serving it with minted new potatoes for an al fresco lunch or with the Celeriac mash on page 48. This is also good with a piece of grilled fish for an autumnal dinner.

1 small head of broccoli, cut into bite size pieces
1 small cauliflower, cut into bite size pieces
For the dressing
1 tablespoon Dijon mustard
4 tablespoons low fat plain yogurt
a small bunch of parsley
salt and freshly ground black pepper

● Bring a large saucepan of lightly salted water to the boil. Add the broccoli and cauliflower and simmer for 4–5 minutes, until just tender.
● Meanwhile place all the dressing ingredients together in bowl and stir together. Drain the vegetables and return to the pan. Pour over the dressing and toss together. Serve.

Courgettes with mint

0 POINTS values per recipe

60 calories per serving

Takes 10 minutes

Serves 2

Ⓨ

This is like an antipasto – good hot, cold or warm. It could be combined with Warm broad bean and smoked ham pittas (page 112) or the Spicy parsnip and leek patties (page 43). You can also use it as an accompaniment to grilled fish or meat, or serve it on its own as a light lunch or supper dish.

low fat cooking spray
3 garlic cloves, chopped finely
450 g (1 lb) courgettes, sliced into thin batons about 2.5 cm
    (1 inch) long
2 tablespoons red or white wine vinegar or balsamic vinegar
2 tablespoons soy sauce
a small bunch of mint, chopped finely

● Heat a large non stick pan or wok and spray with the low fat cooking spray. Stir fry the garlic for a few minutes, until golden and then add the courgettes and stir fry them over a high heat until golden on the edges.
● With the pan still on a high heat quickly pour in the vinegar and soy sauce and stir fry a few seconds to mix it through.
● Remove the pan or wok from the heat and stir in the mint. Serve hot, or allow to cool and eat warm or cool.

Storecupboard laundry...

Replace shop-bought, fat laden salad dressings with your own homemade varieties. Healthy salad dressings are so easy to make and taste better too. You can make creamy varieties as above, or combine balsamic vinegar with a little olive oil or nut oils, such as walnut or sesame.

Aubergine dip

0 *POINTS* value per recipe   Serves 4

55 calories per serving

Takes 15 minutes to prepare, 1 hour to cook

A simple and delicious way of cooking aubergines that retains their full flavour without the use of oil. Serve hot or cold

2 large aubergines
low fat cooking spray
1/2 teaspoon mustard seeds
a bunch of spring onions, chopped finely
100 g (3 1/2 oz) small mushrooms, halved
2 garlic cloves, crushed
1 red chilli, de-seeded and chopped
1 teaspoon cumin seeds
2 teaspoons garam masala
1/2 teaspoon ground turmeric
400 g can of chopped tomatoes
a small bunch of fresh coriander, chopped
salt and freshly ground black pepper

● Preheat the oven to Gas Mark 6/200°C/fan oven 180°C, prick the aubergines with a fork a few times and wrap each one in foil. Bake for 45 minutes to 1 hour, until soft.

● Meanwhile heat a large frying pan and spray with the low fat cooking spray. Fry the mustard seeds for a few minutes until they start to pop and then add the spring onions, mushrooms, garlic and chilli and stir fry for a few minutes.

● Add the other spices and stir fry for 1 minute then add the tomatoes and bring to the boil. Simmer for 5 minutes and then turn off the heat.

● Cut each of the cooked aubergines in half lengthways and scoop out the soft flesh. Mash the flesh briefly in a bowl. Add this to the pan with the fresh coriander and seasoning and fold in. Bring to the boil again and simmer for a few minutes until thick and rich.

Stir fried Savoy cabbage with garlic and chilli

0 *POINTS* values per recipe   Serves 4

80 calories per serving

Takes 15 minutes

A quick and tasty way to cook cabbage. Great served instead of rice or noodles with grilled fish or chicken, sprinkled with soy sauce.

1 Savoy cabbage, quartered and shredded
low fat cooking spray
4 garlic cloves, sliced finely
1 red pepper, de-seeded and diced finely
2 small chillies, de-seeded and sliced finely
4 tablespoons soy sauce
1 teaspoon Tabasco sauce

● Put a small amount of water in the bottom of a large saucepan. Place the cabbage in the pan and cover with a tightly fitting lid. Steam for 4–5 minutes, until tender.

● Heat a large pan or wok and spray with the low fat cooking spray. Stir fry the garlic for a few minutes, until golden and then add the pepper and chillies and stir fry for a few minutes more.

● Add the cabbage, the soy sauce and Tabasco sauce and stir fry on a high heat for two more minutes. Serve.

Food fantastic...

Soluble fibres such as those found in vegetables, such as cabbage and fruits tend to lower cholesterol and blood sugar and so protect against diabetes. Cabbage is also rich in antioxidants which can help protect your body from damage caused by environmental pollutants.

Celeriac mash with onion gravy

6 *POINTS* values per recipe   Serves 4

175 calories per serving

Takes 45 minutes

Good served with low fat sausages, grilled fish or meat.

low fat cooking spray

4 red or white onions, sliced

a small bunch of thyme, tough stems removed, tender stems and leaves chopped

1 celeriac (about 600 g/1 lb 5 oz), peeled and cut into small even sized chunks

500 g (1 lb 2 oz) floury potatoes, such as Red Rooster or Maris Piper, cut into even sized chunks

100 g (3^1/$_2$ oz) virtually fat free fromage frais

300 ml (^{1}/$_2$ pint) vegetable stock

salt and freshly ground black pepper

● Heat a large saucepan and spray with the low fat cooking spray. Add the onions and stir fry for a few minutes. Season, add the thyme and a few tablespoons of water.

● Cover the pan with a sheet of baking parchment and a lid and cook on the lowest heat for 20–30 minutes, until the onions are soft and caramelised, stirring very occasionally and scraping any stuck on bits back in.

● Meanwhile put the celeriac and potatoes in a large saucepan of cold water and bring to the boil. Reduce the heat and simmer for 20 minutes, until the vegetables are tender.

● Drain and return to the pan. Season and mash until smooth and then stir in the fromage frais and keep warm.

● Remove the lid and paper from the onions, turn up the heat and add the stock. Bring to the boil and allow to boil rapidly, stirring and scraping the bottom of the pan, until the gravy is reduced and thickened. Check the seasoning and serve with the mash.

Top tip

Cut potatoes and the celeriac into same size pieces to ensure even cooking.

Aubergine crisps

0 *POINTS* values per recipe   Serves 2

40 calories per serving

Takes 15 minutes

These are a totally delicious alternative to potato crisps and lower in *POINTS* values. They make a great accompaniment to curries like the Tiger prawn curry on page 168 or salad like the Mushroom antipasto on page 121. You can dip them into the Yogurt sauce on page 42 or serve these scattered with cherry tomato halves, rocket leaves and balsamic vinegar.

2 large aubergines, sliced in half widthways and then into 5 mm (¼ inch) thin slices on the diagonal to give you long semi-circles

low fat cooking spray

salt and freshly ground black pepper

● Lay the aubergine slices on the grill pan, spray with the low fat cooking spray and then season liberally. Grill until golden and then turn the slices over. Spray and season again and grill for a further 2–4 minutes until dried out and golden. Serve warm.

Storecupboard laundry...

Try to find imaginative ways to replace your usual fat laden snacks with healthy alternatives to help stay on track. The aubergine crisps above are a great example. Make sweet potato or parsnip chips instead of the shop bought varieties or replace breadsticks with chopped raw carrot, cucumber and celery as an alternative with dips.

Food in a flash

When you're tired after a long day, or just want to relax, the idea of cooking from scratch can be disheartening. It is times like these when it can be tempting to reach for a takeaway menu or grab a microwave meal. But with the right ingredients and know-how, you can create a meal in the time that it takes for fast food delivery – with much more satisfying results.

Simple, fast and fabulous food is what this chapter is all about. With minimum preparation and the meal on the table in less than 30 minutes, you'll find the tasty dishes in this chapter are just the ticket. You'll find an emphasis on stir fries and oriental foods in this chapter, as these are so quick and stress-free, but have wonderful, flavoursome results.

Nasi goreng (page 53)

Glazed pork chops with mushroom ragu

7 *POINTS* values per recipe   Serves 2

270 calories per serving

Takes 30 minutes

These tender pork chops are brushed with a honey and wholegrain mustard glaze and served with a tangy mushroom and tomato ragu.

1 tablespoon runny honey
1 tablespoon wholegrain mustard
4 x 75 g (2¾ oz) lean pork chops, fat removed
For the ragu
low fat cooking spray
1 garlic clove, crushed
200 g (7 oz) mushrooms, chopped
400 g can of chopped tomatoes
½ teaspoon dried herbes de Provence or oregano
a small bunch of basil or parsley, chopped (optional)
salt and freshly ground black pepper

● First make the ragu. Heat a large frying pan and spray with the low fat cooking spray and then fry the garlic for 1 minute. Add the mushrooms and stir fry on a high heat for 5 minutes. Add the tomatoes and dried herbs.

● Bring to the boil and then simmer gently, uncovered, for 10–15 minutes or until thick. Taste and season and stir through the fresh herbs, if using, before serving.

● Preheat the grill. Gently heat the honey and mustard together in a small saucepan and then brush this glaze over the pork chops. Grill the chops on one side for 3–4 minutes.

● Turn them over, brush again with the glaze and grill the other side for a few minutes or until the chops are golden brown and cooked through.

● Serve the chops with any remaining honey and mustard glaze from the grill pan drizzled over and a spoonful of the ragu.

Sweet and sour salmon

25½ *POINTS* values per recipe   Serves 4

455 calories per serving

Takes 20 minutes

100 g (3½ oz) medium egg noodles
6 garlic cloves, crushed
5 cm (2 inch) piece of fresh root ginger, chopped finely
3 tablespoons soy sauce
juice of ½ lemon
2 teaspoons rice or white wine vinegar
1 tablespoon runny honey
2 teaspoons tomato purée
4 x 150 g (5½ oz) salmon fillets, skinned
low fat cooking spray
2 red peppers, de-seeded and sliced into strips
4 medium carrots, sliced into matchsticks
150 g (5½ oz) green beans, topped
a small bunch of spring onions, sliced into 2.5 cm (1 inch) lengths on the diagonal
1 teaspoon sesame oil
a small bunch of coriander, chopped

● Cook the noodles as directed on the packet, drain and set aside. Place half the garlic and half the ginger in a large frying pan with the soy sauce, lemon juice, vinegar, honey and tomato purée and mix together.

● Add the fish, skin side up, baste with the sauce, cover and bring to a gentle simmer. Cook for 10 minutes, until the fish is just cooked through.

● Meanwhile heat a wok or large non stick frying pan and spray with the low fat cooking spray. Add the remaining garlic and ginger and stir fry for 1 minute. Add all the vegetables and stir fry for 3–4 minutes, until they are just tender and golden on the edges.

● Add the noodles and sesame oil to the pan and toss together. Divide the noodle mixture amongst four plates. Top each pile with a piece of fish and pour over the sauce left in the frying pan. Scatter with the fresh coriander and serve.

Nasi goreng

22 POINTS value per recipe

330 calories per serving

Takes 20 minutes

Serves 4

4 teaspoons Indonesian or Thai red curry paste
a bunch of spring onions, chopped
4 garlic cloves, sliced finely
200 g (7 oz) cooked, peeled prawns, defrosted if frozen
600 g (1 lb 5 oz) cooked rice (240 g/8½ oz uncooked weight)
2 tablespoons soy sauce
200 g (7 oz) frozen petit pois
1 tablespoon fish sauce
juice of 1 lime
2 eggs, beaten
a small bunch of coriander, chopped, to serve

● Heat the curry paste in a wok or large frying pan and add the spring onions and garlic. Stir fry for 4–5 minutes, until cooked through.

● Add all the other ingredients, except the eggs and coriander, and stir fry for 5 minutes. Now push everything to one side of the wok or pan and tip the eggs into the gap. Stir them until set, like scrambled egg, then stir into the other ingredients from the side of the pan.

● Scatter with the chopped coriander and serve.

Sort your surroundings...

One of the most common causes of over-eating is because the food is there. And, the reason it is there, is because it was picked up at the supermarket! Try to write out a shopping list for all the foods that you will require for the week, and then make sure you aren't hungry when you shop – so that you'll be less tempted to buy your problem foods.

Sesame chicken

7 POINTS values per recipe　　　　　　　　　　　　**Serves 4**

145 calories per serving

Takes 15 minutes plus marinating

This is great as a light lunch or serve with noodles or rice for a more substantial meal. Don't forget to count the **POINTS** values.

2 skinless, boneless chicken breasts, each weighing approximately
　　150 g/5½ oz, cut in half lengthways
4 garlic cloves, sliced finely
2.5 cm (1 inch) piece of fresh root ginger, grated finely
4 tablespoons soy sauce
zest and juice of 2 limes
2 teaspoons sesame oil
For the spinach salad
225 g (8 oz) baby spinach leaves
a small bunch of mint, chopped roughly
1 bunch of spring onions, sliced finely lengthways

● Lay the chicken breasts between two pieces of baking parchment, clingfilm or foil and pound with a rolling pin until they become thin escalopes.

● Place the garlic, ginger, soy sauce, lime zest and juice and sesame oil in a large bowl and add the chicken breasts. Toss the chicken in the marinade and then set aside for at least 5 minutes but preferably 30 minutes.

● Meanwhile divide the spinach, mint and spring onions between four serving plates or bowls.

● Remove the chicken from the marinade and grill for 4–5 minutes on each side, or until cooked through and golden. Slice the chicken and place on top of the spinach salad.

● Heat the leftover marinade in a small pan until boiling, then drizzle over the chicken and salad before serving.

Spicy lamb chops with fattoush

14 POINTS values per recipe　　　　　　　　　　　**Serves 2**

590 calories per serving

Takes 20 minutes

Fattoush is a Syrian and Lebanese salad of chopped salad vegetables with herbs and lemon and toasted flatbread. This makes a delicious, quick and healthy midweek supper.

1 teaspoon cumin seeds, crushed
¼ teaspoon dried chilli flakes or small red chilli, de-seeded and
　　chopped finely
zest and juice of 1 lemon
4 x 100 g (3½ oz) lamb chops on the bone, trimmed of any fat
For the fattoush
2 pitta breads, torn into pieces
1 Little Gem lettuce, shredded
4 spring onions, sliced finely
½ cucumber, diced finely
1 green pepper, de-seeded and diced finely
2 ripe tomatoes, diced
zest and juice of 1 lemon
a few sprigs of mint, chopped
a few sprigs of coriander, chopped
a few sprigs of parsley, chopped
salt and freshly ground black pepper

● Place the cumin seeds, chilli and lemon zest and juice on a plate and rub the lamb chops in the mixture. Keep the lamb chops in the fridge while you make the salad.

● To make the fattoush, preheat the oven to Gas Mark 7/220°C/ fan oven 200°C and spread out the pitta pieces on a baking tray. Toast in the oven for 10 minutes, or until crisp.

● Meanwhile combine all the other fattoush ingredients in a bowl.

● Grill the lamb chops for about 5–6 minutes on each side, until cooked as preferred. Toss the toasted pitta pieces into the salad and serve with the chops.

Grilled trout with Chinese vegetables

6 POINTS VALUE

12 *POINTS* values per recipe   Serves 2

300 calories per serving

Takes 20 minutes

The fragrant stuffing for this grilled trout is also used as the accompanying salad.

2 x 250 g (9 oz) whole trout
salt and freshly ground black pepper
For the stuffing
5 cm (2 inch) piece of fresh root ginger, sliced into matchsticks
a bunch of spring onions, sliced into thin strips
100 g (3½ oz) mange tout peas, sliced into thin strips
2 medium carrots, sliced into thin strips
2 tablespoons soy sauce or tamari sauce
1 teaspoon sesame oil
a small bunch of coriander, chopped

- Mix together all the stuffing ingredients in a bowl.
- Season the trout, inside and out, and then place a small handful of the stuffing inside the cavity of each one. Grill for 5–10 minutes on each side, until cooked through and golden. Serve with the remaining salad.

Food fantastic...

Fish is a great source of Vitamin E, which contributes to the healthy condition of your skin and also helps to fight free radicals (these are unbalanced molecules that can cause damage to your cells).

Mexican rice

6½ POINTS VALUE

26½ *POINTS* values per recipe   Serves 4

305 calories per serving

Takes 25 minutes

Hot and fiery, this dish will put you in the mood for a fiesta!

low fat cooking spray
1 teaspoon cumin seeds
2 red onions, chopped finely
3 garlic cloves, crushed
2 small red chillies, de-seeded and chopped finely
300 g (10½ oz) rice
2 red or orange peppers, de-seeded and diced finely
600 ml (1 pint) hot vegetable stock
1 tablespoon Worcestershire sauce
1 tablespoon tomato purée
100 g (3½ oz) frozen peas
100 g (3½ oz) salami, sliced into strips
250 g (9 oz) cherry tomatoes, halved
a small bunch of coriander, chopped
salt and freshly ground black pepper

- Heat a large saucepan and spray with the low fat cooking spray. Fry the cumin seeds until they start to pop. Add the onions and garlic and a tablespoon of water and stir fry for a few minutes, until golden and softened.
- Add the chillies, rice, peppers, stock, Worcestershire sauce and tomato purée and stir together. Cover the pan and simmer on a low heat for 10–15 minutes, until the rice is very nearly cooked.
- Add the peas and cover again for 2 minutes. Now add the salami and tomatoes and stir through. Season and scatter with the fresh coriander before serving.

(4) Pad Thai

15½ *POINTS* values per recipe | Serves 4

285 calories per serving

Takes 30 minutes

200 g (7 oz) rice noodles
low fat cooking spray
2 teaspoons Thai spice paste
150 g (5½ oz) 12–16 (approximately) cooked, shelled tiger prawns
500 g (1 lb 2 oz) zero green vegetables e.g. pak choi, Chinese
   leaves, watercress, spinach, broccoli, mangetout peas, green
   beans, beansprouts
2 tablespoons soy sauce
a small bunch of coriander, chopped, to garnish
25 g (1 oz) peanuts, toasted and chopped, to garnish

● Bring a large saucepan of water to the boil and then take off
the heat. Add the rice noodles and leave to soak as directed on the
packet or until just tender. Drain and refresh under cold water but
reserve a little of the soaking water. Place in a bowl and snip with
scissors to make shorter lengths.
● Heat a large frying pan or wok and spray with the low fat cooking
spray. Add the spice paste and stir fry for about 30 seconds, until it
becomes fragrant then add the prawns and stir fry for 2 minutes.
● Add the vegetables, soy sauce and stir fry together, with a few
tablespoons of the reserved noodle soaking water, until the
vegetables are tender.
● Add the noodles to the mixture, toss together and heat
through. Serve garnished with the coriander and peanuts.

Time saver...

*Stir fries are fantastic, flavoursome and a very quick dish to make. Most
supermarkets now sell ready prepared fresh stir fried vegetables quite cheaply,
so that you can just throw the whole packet into the pan for a quick and tasty
meal – rather than chopping and preparing your own.*

(2) Sticky marmalade turkey escalopes

8 *POINTS* values per recipe | Serves 4

295 calories per serving

Takes 15 minutes to prepare, 20 minutes to cook

You may be more used to marmalade on your toast, but it is
utterly delicious on lean escalopes as it caramelises to a sweet
and sour sauce.

4 x 100 g (3½ oz) turkey escalopes
1 tablespoon reduced sugar marmalade or orange jam
low fat cooking spray
2 garlic cloves, sliced finely
1 red onion, sliced finely
2 large green courgettes, sliced into thin batons
2 large yellow courgettes (use green if you can't find these),
   sliced into thin batons
zest and juice of 2 oranges
a small bunch of parsley, chopped finely
salt and freshly ground black pepper

● Season the turkey escalopes and spread them with the marmalade
or jam on both sides.
● Spray a large frying pan with the low fat cooking spray and fry
the garlic and onion until softened, adding a few tablespoons of
water, if necessary, to stop them sticking.
● Add the courgettes to the pan and squeeze over the juice and
zest of one orange.
● Continue to stir fry over a high heat until the courgettes are
golden on the edges and just softened. Tip out into a serving bowl
and keep warm.
● Spray the pan again with low fat cooking spray and fry the
turkey escalopes over a gentle heat for 3–4 minutes on each side,
until golden and cooked through. Remove from the pan on to
serving plates and turn up the heat.
● Squeeze the remaining orange juice and zest into the hot pan
and stir in the parsley. Season and simmer for a few seconds,
scraping any stuck on juices into the sauce, before pouring over
the escalopes. Serve with the courgettes.

Creamy turkey crêpes

12½ POINTS values per recipe

530 calories per serving

Takes 20 minutes

Serves 2

This recipe takes advantage of the ready made crêpes that you can buy from supermarkets. The filling is quick, easy and tasty.

4 ready made crêpes
low fat cooking spray
200 g (7 oz) turkey fillets, sliced into thin strips
2 tablespoons soy sauce
1 red pepper, de-seeded and sliced finely
2 small courgettes, sliced into thin strips
100 ml (3½ fl oz) vegetable stock
100 g (3½ oz) low fat soft cheese
salt and freshly ground black pepper

● Wrap the crêpes in foil and place in a warm oven to heat through. Spray a large non stick frying pan with the low fat cooking spray. Stir fry the turkey strips for 5 minutes, until nearly cooked through and golden.

● Add the soy sauce, pepper and courgettes. Stir fry for another 2 minutes or until the vegetables begin to soften. Stir in the stock and soft cheese.

● Check the seasoning and divide the mixture between the warmed crêpes. Roll them up and serve.

Fridge laundry...

Replace cream cheese with low fat soft cheeses, such as Philadelphia extra light. However, always check the pack carefully to make sure that it says low fat soft cheese and not medium fat soft cheese, as sometimes the labelling can be deceptive.

Stir fried pork with baby sweetcorn

7 POINTS values per recipe

180 calories per serving

Takes 20 minutes

Serves 4

A super fresh and crunchy stir fry, full of wonderful flavours and textures that make a healthy and satisfying lunch or dinner.

low fat cooking spray
300 g (10½ oz) pork fillet, trimmed of all fat and sliced into 5 mm (¼ inch) thick medallions
4 carrots, sliced into matchsticks
300 g (10½ oz) baby sweetcorn, halved lengthways
150 g (5½ oz) sugar snap peas, halved diagonally
2 tablespoons tomato purée mixed with 4 tablespoons of water to make a thin paste
4 tablespoons soy sauce
2 garlic cloves, crushed
2.5 cm (1 inch) piece of fresh root ginger, grated finely
1 tablespoon runny honey
2 tablespoons white, red or rice wine vinegar
a small bunch of chives or coriander, chopped
salt and freshly ground black pepper

● Heat a large frying pan or wok and spray with the low fat cooking spray. Season and stir fry the pork for 5 minutes, until golden brown and just cooked through.

● Add the carrots, baby sweetcorn and sugar snap peas and stir fry for another couple of minutes, until the vegetables are golden on the edges.

● In a small bowl, whisk together all the other ingredients except the chives or coriander with 100 ml of cold water and pour into the pan. Stir fry for a further 2 minutes until the sauce is reduced and thickened. Serve scattered with the chives or coriander.

Hot beef noodles

10½ *POINTS* values per recipe
390 calories per serving
Takes 25 minutes

Serves 2

No one will guess that this is a Weight Watchers recipe – succulent strips of beef with bright vegetables and noodles and a tasty sauce. It makes a supremely quick meal and needs no accompaniment.

low fat cooking spray
200 g (7 oz) beef steak, trimmed of all fat and sliced into thin strips
2 shallots or 1 red onion, sliced finely
1 garlic clove, sliced finely
1 red pepper, de-seeded and sliced
½ head of broccoli, sliced into florets
½ teaspoon Tabasco sauce
2 tablespoons Worcestershire sauce
2 tablespoons soy sauce
600 ml (1 pint) vegetable stock
100 g (3½ oz) thin or medium egg noodles
a small bunch of coriander, chopped (optional)
salt and freshly ground black pepper

● Spray a large non stick frying pan or wok with the low fat cooking spray. Season and stir fry the beef strips until they are browned all over. Remove to a plate and set aside.

● Spray the pan again and add the shallots or onion and garlic and stir fry for 2–4 minutes, adding a little water to stop them sticking, until golden and softened.

● Add the pepper and broccoli and stir fry for a few minutes until golden on the edges then add the beef, Tabasco sauce, Worcestershire sauce, soy sauce, stock and noodles.

● Cover the pan, bring to the boil and simmer for 5 minutes, until the sauce is reduced a little and the noodles tender. Serve scattered with coriander, if using.

Food fantastic...

Red peppers are not only delicious, but are also a good source of vitamin C and beta-carotene. Use peppers in stir fries, casseroles or roasted. They are also excellent stuffed and baked.

Mushroom and ham tagliatelle

13 *POINTS* values per recipe   Serves 2

365 calories per serving

Takes 15–20 minutes

Serve this pasta dish with a big crunchy salad of crisp lettuce, cherry tomatoes and red pepper strips, seasoned and drizzled with a little balsamic vinegar.

175 g (6 oz) tagliatelle, dried
low fat cooking spray
200 g (7 oz) mushrooms, sliced
juice of 1/2 a lemon
3 tablespoons virtually fat free fromage frais
150 g (51/2 oz) lean ham, all fat removed, cut into strips
salt and freshly ground black pepper
a small bunch of chives, chopped finely, to garnish (optional)

● Cook the pasta in plenty of boiling water, as directed on the pack. Meanwhile heat a large frying pan and then spray with the low fat cooking spray.
● Add the mushrooms, season and stir fry on a high heat for 3 minutes until they are soft and have re-absorbed all their juices. Add the lemon juice, then add 100 ml (31/2 fl oz) cold water, stir, scraping up any stuck on juices. Take the pan off the heat and stir in the fromage frais, ham and seasoning.
● Drain the pasta leaving a few tablespoons of the remaining cooking liquid remaining. Toss the pasta in the ham and mushroom sauce and check the seasoning. Serve garnished with chopped chives, if using.

Top tip

When making pasta sauces always try to reserve a few tablespoons of the pasta cooking liquid to add to the sauce. It improves the sauce's texture and helps it to bind it to the pasta.

Stir fried broccoli and tofu

4 *POINTS* values per recipe   Serves 2

205 calories per serving

Takes 15 minutes

For this dish you need the smoked tofu available from the chiller section of larger supermarkets or from health or Asian food shops.

low fat cooking spray
2 garlic cloves, sliced finely
2.5 cm (1 inch) piece of fresh root ginger, chopped finely
150 g (51/2 oz) smoked tofu pieces
1 large carrot, cut into matchsticks
1 head broccoli, cut into florets and the stem diced
4 tablespoons soy sauce
juice of 1/2 a lemon
150 ml (1/4 pint) vegetable stock
a small bunch of coriander, chopped

● Heat a large frying pan or wok and spray with the low fat cooking spray. Stir fry the garlic and ginger for a few moments until they turn golden.
● Add the tofu and the vegetables and stir fry them together. Add the soy sauce, lemon juice and the stock and mix together.
● Stir fry for a further 2–4 minutes, until most of the liquid has evaporated and the vegetables are al dente then serve scattered with coriander.

Storecupboard basics...

Soy sauce is an essential condiment, particularly if you like Oriental foods. You can use it to colour and flavour marinades, dips and sauces. Light soy sauce has a delicate, salty flavour that goes well with white meats and seafood. Use dark soy sauce (which is thicker, richer but less salty) with meats or in stews.

Chicken with cannellini beans and rosemary

4½ POINTS VALUE

8½ *POINTS* values per recipe · Serves 2

275 calories per serving

Takes 20 minutes

Serve on its own or with a crisp green salad.

low fat cooking spray
200 g (7 oz) chicken breast fillets, sliced into small pieces
1 garlic clove, chopped finely
½ teaspoon cumin seeds
a small bunch of rosemary, tough stems removed, chopped
juice and zest of ½ a lemon
400 g can of cannellini beans, drained and rinsed
200 g (7 oz) cherry tomatoes, halved
100 ml (3½ fl oz) vegetable stock
2 tablespoons virtually fat free fromage frais
salt and freshly ground black pepper
a small bunch of parsley or basil, chopped, to garnish (optional)

● Heat a large frying pan or wok then spray with the low fat cooking spray. Season and stir fry the chicken for 4–5 minutes until golden brown and cooked through.

● Add the garlic and cumin seeds and stir fry until fragrant. Add the rosemary, lemon, beans, tomatoes, stock and seasoning and stir to combine. Bring to the boil and simmer, covered for 5 minutes. Remove from heat and allow to cool for a minute or two then fold in the fromage frais and scatter with parsley or basil to garnish, if using.

Time saver...

If the idea of juicing your own lemons doesn't sound appealing, then buy a bottle of Jif Lemon Juice. It is made from real lemons, and tastes almost as good as the real thing. A tablespoon of Jif is equal to a tablespoon of squeezed lemon – and you can just keep it in your storecupboard for when you need it.

Cod parcels with lemon and dill sauce

2½ POINTS VALUE

9½ *POINTS* values per recipe · Serves 4

150 calories per serving

Takes 25 minutes

This is a lovely, easy way to cook fish as the flavours are sealed in during cooking and each person opens their own parcel. The lemon and dill sauce goes well with plain grilled fillets of fish or chicken breasts.

1 bulb fennel, sliced finely
4 x 150 g (5½ oz) cod steaks
juice and zest of 1 lemon
salt and freshly ground black pepper
For the sauce
low fat cooking spray
2 shallots, sliced finely
juice and zest of 1 lemon
a small bunch of dill, chopped finely
6 tablespoons virtually fat free fromage frais

● Preheat the oven to Gas Mark 6/200°C/fan oven 180°C. Cut four pieces of baking parchment, each about 30 cm (12 inches) square. Divide the fennel into four and pile in the centre of each piece of paper.

● Lay a fish steak on top of each pile, season, and squeeze over the lemon juice and scatter with the lemon zest. Lift up the opposite sides of the baking parchment, bring them together at the top and fold over a few times to seal. Fold over the open ends and tuck underneath the fish to make a sealed parcel.

● Place the parcels on a baking tray and bake for 15 minutes, until just cooked through. Meanwhile make the sauce. Spray a small saucepan with the low fat cooking spray and stir fry the shallots with a couple of tablespoons of water, until softened.

● Squeeze in the lemon juice and allow to bubble, and then remove from the heat and stir in the lemon zest, dill and fromage frais. Season and serve with the fish.

Turkey and mango noodle salad

18½ *POINTS* values per recipe   Serves 4

315 calories per serving

Takes 25 minutes

125 g (4½ oz) mung bean vermicelli (glass noodles)

low fat cooking spray

4 garlic cloves, chopped finely

400 g (14 oz) turkey mince

2.5 cm (1 inch) piece of fresh root ginger, chopped finely

1 or 2 small red chillies, de-seeded and chopped finely

a bunch of spring onions, chopped finely

juice of 2 limes

4 tablespoons soy sauce

100 ml (3½ fl oz) vegetable stock

2 ripe mangoes, peeled, stoned and sliced

a small bunch of fresh coriander, chopped

a few sprigs of mint, chopped

2 Little Gem lettuces, shredded

4 lime wedges, to serve

● Cover the noodles with boiling water for 5 minutes, or as directed on the packet, then drain, place in a bowl and roughly chop with scissors.

● Heat a large frying pan or wok and spray with the low fat cooking spray. Stir fry the garlic for a few seconds, until golden and then fry the turkey mince, breaking up with a wooden spatula, for 4 minutes until browned.

● Add the ginger, chillies, spring onions, noodles, lime juice, soy sauce and vegetable stock. Stir together and heat through for 2 minutes.

● Remove from the heat and stir through the sliced mango, coriander and mint. Place a pile of lettuce on each serving plate or bowl and spoon on the noodles. Serve with lime wedges to squeeze over.

Smoked haddock and new potatoes in mustard sauce

7½ *POINTS* values per recipe   Serves 2

343 calories per serving

Takes 25 minutes

A robust, vibrantly flavoured supper that's quick and easy to prepare in one pan.

200 g (7 oz) new potatoes, halved

200 g (7 oz) smoked haddock fillet

low fat cooking spray

4 medium leeks, sliced finely

2 teaspoons wholegrain Dijon mustard

200 g (7 oz) virtually fat free fromage frais

juice of ½ a lemon

a small bunch of fresh tarragon or parsley, chopped finely, (optional)

salt and freshly ground black pepper

● Cook the new potatoes for 15–20 minutes in a pan of lightly salted boiling water, until tender and then drain.

● Place the haddock fillet skin side down on a foil-lined grill pan and grill for 5–10 minutes until opaque and cooked through.

● Meanwhile heat a large saucepan and spray with the low fat cooking spray. Stir fry the leeks for a few minutes and then add a couple of tablespoons of water; cover and leave to cook on a low heat for 5 minutes, or until softened.

● Add all the other ingredients to the pan including the cooked potatoes. Then flake in the cooked haddock, removing the skin first. Gently fold together. Check the seasoning and heat through then serve.

Fresh pasta with creamy watercress sauce

21 *POINTS* values per recipe

350 calories per serving

Takes 15 minutes

Serves 4

400 g (14 oz) fresh pasta shapes
low fat cooking spray
4 garlic cloves, sliced finely
175 g (6 oz) watercress, washed and chopped roughly
150 g (5½ oz) plain low fat soft cheese or with herbs and garlic
zest from ½ lemon
1 teaspoon dried chilli flakes (optional)
150 ml (¼ pint) skimmed milk
salt and freshly ground black pepper

● Cook the pasta as directed on the packet in plenty of lightly
salted, boiling water until it is al dente.

● Meanwhile spray a large frying pan with the low fat cooking
spray and fry the garlic slices until golden. Add the watercress and
cover the pan for a few minutes, stirring occasionally until wilted.

● Add the soft cheese, lemon zest, seasoning, chilli, if using, milk
and the drained pasta with a few tablespoons of the pasta cooking
liquid. Gently fold together and serve.

Chicken noodles

13½ *POINTS* values per recipe

315 calories per serving

Takes 15 minutes to prepare, 15 minutes to cook

Serves 4

A quick dish that is delicious without the chicken, too.

200 g (7 oz) rice noodles
low fat cooking spray
a bunch of spring onions, sliced
4 garlic cloves, sliced thinly
200 g (7 oz) chicken breast, sliced thinly
150 g (5½ oz) beansprouts
2 large carrots, peeled and sliced into matchsticks
150 g (5½ oz) mange tout peas, sliced thinly
1 red pepper, de-seeded and sliced finely
4 tablespoons soy sauce
1 tablespoon Worcestershire sauce
100 ml (3½ fl oz) vegetable or chicken stock
2 limes

● Soak the rice noodles in boiling water as directed on the packet.

● Spray a large frying pan or wok with the low fat cooking spray
and stir fry the spring onions and garlic for 1–2 minutes, adding a
tablespoon of water if necessary to stop them sticking. Add the
chicken and stir fry for a few minutes, until browned all over.

● Add all the other ingredients, including the noodles (except the
limes), and stir fry for a final few minutes, tossing together to mix
everything well.

● Squeeze over the juice of one lime and cut the other into
wedges. Serve the noodles with the lime wedges.

One pot wonders

A fantastic secret to managing a healthy lifestyle is to minimise the washing up. It is surprising what wonderful meals you can create in just one pot. The cooking time is often a little bit longer, but the minimal preparation and clearing up, along with succulent, sensational results make the waiting time worth it.

This chapter has an array of superb one pot dishes from comforting, tender casseroles and stews to warm and spicy curries that really take full advantage of all the flavours used. And it emphasises just how easy cooking (and clearing up afterwards) can be.

Sausage and bean stew

8½ *POINTS* values per recipe

175 calories per serving

Takes 25 minutes

Serves 4

There are endless variations to this hearty soup. Try it with borlotti or kidney beans or use spicy sausages and whatever herbs are in season.

low fat cooking spray

4 thin low fat sausages

1 small onion, chopped finely

1 garlic clove, crushed

400 g can kidney beans, drained and rinsed

1 carrot, diced

1 celery stick, sliced finely

1 bay leaf

300 ml (½ pint) vegetable stock

300 ml (½ pint) passata

a small bunch of rosemary, leaves stripped from the stalks and chopped finely

salt and freshly ground black pepper

● Spray a large flameproof casserole dish with the low fat cooking spray. Fry the sausages and onion with the garlic, until golden.

● Add all the other ingredients, bring to the boil and then simmer for 10 minutes.

● Lift the sausages from the pan and slice them thickly. Return them to the stew. Check the seasoning and serve.

Top tip

It is cheaper to use dried beans and soak them overnight in plenty of cold water. Cook them making sure you boil them for 15 minutes and then simmer for 30 minutes, or until tender. Do not season before or during the cooking process as this will cause the bean skins to toughen. Beans like these borlotti beans are packed with protein, vitamins, minerals and fibre.

Jamaican black beans

3 *POINTS* values per recipe

325 calories per serving

Takes 20 minutes to prepare, 1¼ hours to cook, plus soaking

Serves 4

This dish has the vibrant colours of the Caribbean combined with hot and spicy flavours.

225 g (8 oz) dried black beans, soaked overnight in plenty of cold water, drained and rinsed

1 bay leaf

low fat cooking spray

1 large onion, chopped finely

2 garlic cloves, crushed

1 teaspoon English mustard powder or mustard

1 tablespoon black treacle

a small bunch of thyme, tough stems removed, tender stems and leaves, chopped

1 small red chilli, de-seeded and chopped finely

400 ml (14 fl oz) vegetable stock

1 red pepper, de-seeded and diced

1 yellow pepper, de-seeded and diced

1 x 1 kg (2 lb 4 oz) butternut squash, peeled, de-seeded and chopped into 1 cm (½ inch) dice

salt and freshly ground black pepper

● Place the beans in a large saucepan or flameproof casserole dish and cover with water. Add the bay leaf and bring to the boil. Boil rapidly for 10 minutes, removing the scum as it collects on the surface with a slotted spoon. Reduce the heat and simmer, covered, for a further 30 minutes, until tender. Drain and set aside.

● Spray the pan or casserole dish with the low fat cooking spray and stir fry the onion and garlic for a few minutes, until softened, adding a little water, if necessary, to stop them sticking.

● Add all the other ingredients, including the beans, and stir together. Cover and bring to the boil, and then uncover and simmer for 45 minutes, until all the vegetables are tender and the sauce thickened. Check the seasoning and serve.

Vegetable balti

3½ *POINTS* values per recipe

190 calories per serving

Takes 20 minutes to prepare, 30 minutes to cook

Serves 4

Great flavours and none of the fat associated with a takeaway equivalent. This curry keeps well in the fridge for a few days or could be made in advance and frozen.

low fat cooking spray
2 large onions, sliced finely
4 garlic cloves, crushed
2.5 cm (1 inch) piece of fresh root ginger, chopped finely
1 small red chilli, de-seeded and chopped (optional)
½ teaspoon cumin seeds, crushed
1 teaspoon coriander seeds, crushed
1 tablespoon garam masala
200 g (7 oz) potatoes, peeled and diced
4 medium carrots, peeled and chopped
1 small cauliflower, chopped into florets
400 g can chopped tomatoes
300 ml (½ pint) vegetable stock
200 g (7 oz) green beans, chopped
150 g (5½ oz) low fat plain yogurt
salt and freshly ground black pepper
a small bunch of fresh coriander, chopped, to garnish (optional)

● Heat a large non stick frying pan and spray with the low fat cooking spray. Stir fry the onions for 5 minutes and season them, adding a little water to stop them sticking and help them soften. Mix in the garlic, ginger, chilli, if using, and spices and cook for a further 2 minutes.

● Add the potatoes, carrots, cauliflower, tomatoes and stock, stir together and bring to the boil. Turn down the heat and then simmer for 20 minutes. Add the beans and simmer a further 5 minutes or until the sauce is thick.

● Remove the pan from the heat and allow to cool a little before stirring in the yogurt and fresh coriander, if using, and serve.

Sweet vegetable stew

11½ *POINTS* values per recipe

310 calories per serving

Takes 1 hour

Serves 4

Loosely based on the Argentinian dish Carbonado Criolla, this recipe combines sweet and savoury for a satisfying and filling stew.

low fat cooking spray
1 onion, chopped finely
2 garlic cloves, crushed
300 g (10½ oz) Quorn pieces
1 red chilli, de-seeded and chopped finely
2 medium tomatoes, chopped roughly
1 bay leaf
300 ml (½ pint) vegetable stock
250 ml (9 fl oz) passata
450 g (1 lb) sweet potatoes, peeled and cut into large wedges
1 butternut squash, peeled, de-seeded and cut into large wedges
2 ripe pears, peeled, cored and quartered
salt and freshly ground black pepper
a small bunch of parsley, chopped, to garnish (optional)

● Heat a large flameproof casserole dish and then spray with the low fat cooking spray and stir fry the onion and garlic for a few minutes until softened, adding a little water, if necessary, to stop them sticking.

● Add all the other ingredients except the parsley and bring to the boil. Reduce the heat and simmer for 45 minutes.

● Serve with a scattering of chopped parsley, if using.

Fridge laundry...

Butternut squash is a great alternative to potatoes, when you want to get more vegetables into your diet. Try roasting or boiling and mashing – it's a very versatile vegetable.

Spaghetti Napoli

17 *POINTS* values per recipe | Serves 4

365 calories per serving

Takes 30 minutes | (sauce only) ❋

A classic thick tomato sauce for pasta. Serve with a green salad of interesting fresh leaves like rocket, cos, chicory and oakleaf with cucumber, radishes and sugar snap peas. Sprinkle over a squeeze of lemon juice and seasoning.

350 g (12 oz) spaghetti
low fat cooking spray
1 large onion, peeled and chopped
2 garlic cloves, peeled and crushed
2 x 400 g cans of chopped tomatoes
200 g (7 oz) cherry tomatoes, halved
1 teaspoon artificial sweetener
1 teaspoon dried oregano
a small bunch of fresh parsley or basil (optional)
salt and freshly ground black pepper

● Cook the pasta in plenty of boiling, salted water as directed on the packet, until just cooked through.
● Meanwhile, spray a large frying pan with the low fat cooking spray and fry the onion and garlic for about 5 minutes until softened, adding a few tablespoons of water if they begin to stick.
● Add the chopped tomatoes and cherry tomatoes, sweetener, oregano and seasoning. Stir together and bring to the boil, and then simmer for 15–20 minutes until thick.
● Drain the pasta and add it to the sauce along with 4 tablespoons of the cooking water. Stir together until the pasta is well coated with the sauce. Serve sprinkled with fresh herbs, if using.

Italian fish stew

6½ *POINTS* values per recipe | Serves 4

180 calories per serving

Takes 15 minutes to prepare, 30 minutes to cook

Great to make in the summer when tomatoes are cheap and plentiful and full of flavour. Try this served with the Green beans with rosemary on page 38.

low fat cooking spray
1 large onion, peeled and chopped finely
2 garlic cloves, crushed
2 red peppers canned in brine, chopped
2 x 400 g cans of chopped tomatoes
300 ml (½ pint) vegetable stock
a pinch of saffron strands, soaked in a few tablespoons of boiling water for 30 minutes
2 bay leaves
a small bunch of basil, chopped
½ teaspoon Tabasco sauce
1 tablespoon tomato purée
450 g (1 lb) cod fillets, skinned and cut into even, bite size chunks
8 large cooked prawns, shelled
salt and freshly ground black pepper

● Heat a large saucepan and spray with the low fat cooking spray. Stir fry the onion and garlic, adding a little water if necessary to stop them sticking, for 5 minutes or until the onions have softened.
● Stir in the peppers and tomatoes and add the stock, saffron strands with the soaking liquid, bay leaves, half the basil, Tabasco sauce, tomato purée and seasoning. Bring to the boil and then simmer for 20 minutes
● Add the cod and cook, covered, for a further 5 minutes. Then gently fold in the prawns and allow to heat through. Check the seasoning and scatter with the remaining basil to serve.

(2) Lemon and mint chickpeas

8½ *POINTS* values per recipe

100 calories per serving

Takes 15 minutes

Serves 4

Chickpeas are fantastic at soaking up flavours and make a delicious and nutritious alternative to pasta or rice. Try this dish with something from the Vibrant Veggies chapter such as the Roasted stuffed mushrooms on page 42.

low fat cooking spray
½ teaspoon cumin seeds
1 large onion, chopped finely
2 garlic cloves, crushed
2.5 cm (1 inch) piece of fresh root ginger, peeled and chopped finely
400 g can of chickpeas, drained and rinsed
zest and juice of ½ a lemon
100 ml (3½ fl oz) vegetable stock
a large bunch of mint, chopped
a pinch of freshly grated nutmeg
2 tablespoons virtually fat free fromage frais
salt and freshly ground black pepper

● Heat a large saucepan, spray with the low fat cooking spray and fry the cumin seeds until they pop. Add the onion, garlic and ginger and a few tablespoons of water. Stir fry for a few minutes or until the onion is soft.

● Add the chickpeas, lemon zest and juice, stock, mint, nutmeg and seasoning and stir together. Cook, covered, for 5 minutes and then stir in the fromage frais. Good served hot or cold.

Sort your surroundings...

Trying out new, more unusual combinations like in the recipe above, is a great way to maintain your motivation when losing weight. Relish everything that you put in your mouth, and ask yourself if you are really enjoying it. Cultivate your likes, and experiment with new flavours and textures.

(3) Tuscan beans

6½ *POINTS* values per recipe

200 calories per serving

Takes 20 minutes

Serves 2

Good served on its own or with a crunchy salad of mixed leaves, vine ripened tomatoes and slithers of red onion tossed with a drizzle of balsamic vinegar and seasoning.

low fat cooking spray
1 small onion, chopped finely
1 garlic clove, crushed
½ red pepper, de-seeded and chopped finely
100 g (3½ oz) mushrooms, chopped finely
1 courgette, diced finely
a small bunch of rosemary, woody stems removed, tender stems and leaves chopped
150 g (5½ oz) tomato passata
400 g can of pinto beans, drained and rinsed
salt and freshly ground black pepper
a small bunch of flat leaf parsley, chopped, to garnish (optional)

● Heat a large saucepan and spray with the low fat cooking spray. Fry the onion and garlic for 5 minutes with a few tablespoons of water, until softened.

● Add the pepper, mushrooms and courgette and stir fry again for a few minutes then add the rosemary and passata.

● Stir together and then add the beans and seasoning to the pan. Simmer for 5 minutes and serve scattered with the parsley, if using.

Chicken goulash with dumplings

18½ POINTS values per recipe   **Serves 4**

315 calories per serving

Takes 25 minutes to prepare, 45 minutes to cook

The delicious light dumplings are made with cottage cheese and polenta. They are the perfect accompaniment to this delicious stew.

For the dumplings

1 egg, beaten

250 g (9 oz) cottage cheese

50 g (1¾ oz) quick cook polenta

salt and freshly ground black pepper

For the goulash

low fat cooking spray

4 x 150 g (5½ oz) skinless, boneless chicken breasts

1 onion, chopped finely

2 leeks, chopped

2 celery sticks, chopped

3 garlic cloves, crushed

2 medium tomatoes, chopped roughly

a small bunch of fresh thyme, tough stems removed and leaves and tender stems chopped

600 ml (1 pint) vegetable or chicken stock

bay leaf

1 teaspoon paprika

● Make the dumplings first by stirring the egg into the cottage cheese and then gently folding in the polenta and seasoning. Cover and chill for at least 20 minutes.

● For the goulash, heat a large flameproof casserole dish and spray with the low fat cooking spray. Season the chicken and fry on both sides until golden brown.

● Add the onion, leeks, celery, garlic, tomatoes, thyme, stock and bay leaf. Bring to the boil and then simmer for 45 minutes.

● Meanwhile shape the dumpling mixture into eight golf-ball sized dumplings using wet hands to stop them sticking.

● Stir the paprika into the stew and then gently place the dumplings on top. Cover and steam for a further 5–10 minutes and then serve.

1½ POINTS VALUE

Lemon chicken and chicory

6½ *POINTS* values per recipe   Serves 4

145 calories per serving

Takes 45 minutes

An easy one pot meal with lovely sharp, clean flavours.

low fat cooking spray
2 garlic cloves, crushed
4 x 100 g (3½ oz) skinless, boneless chicken breast fillets
zest and juice of 1 lemon
8 heads of chicory, trimmed of the root end and each head cut in
    half lengthways with the bitter end core scooped out
250 ml (9 fl oz) vegetable stock
a small bunch of parsley, chopped roughly
200 g (7 oz) cherry tomatoes, quartered
salt and freshly ground black pepper

● Preheat the oven to Gas Mark 4/180°C/fan oven 160°C. Heat a large flameproof casserole dish and spray it with the low fat cooking spray.

● Fry the garlic for a few seconds and then add the chicken fillets. Season and squeeze over the lemon juice. Allow the chicken to brown all over before removing to a plate.

● Spray the casserole dish again with low fat cooking spray and fry the chicory on its cut side. Season and turn them until they are browned all over. Pour over the stock and then lay the chicken on top.

● Scatter over half the parsley and the lemon zest, cover and put in the oven to cook for 35 minutes or until the chicken is cooked through and the chicory is tender.

● Season the tomatoes in a small bowl and mix with the remaining parsley before scattering them over the chicken and chicory. Serve immediately.

 5½ POINTS VALUE

Italian grilled chicken with sage and beans

11 *POINTS* values per recipe   Serves 2

355 calories per serving   (the beans without the chicken) ❄

Takes 20 minutes

Cannellini beans cooked like this with sage are well known in Tuscany where they accompany roast meat.

2 x 150 g (5½ oz) skinless, boneless chicken breasts
low fat cooking spray
2 teaspoons dried herbes de Provence or Mediterranean herbs
1 large onion, chopped finely
1 garlic clove, chopped finely
a small bunch of sage, chopped
1 bay leaf
400 g can of cannellini, pinto, red kidney or borlotti beans,
    drained and rinsed
zest and juice of 1 lemon
150 g (5½ oz) green beans cut into 2.5 cm (1 inch) lengths
100 ml (3½ fl oz) vegetable stock
salt and freshly ground black pepper

● Slice the chicken breasts in half horizontally to make four thinner fillets. Season and spray the chicken fillets with the low fat cooking spray and then sprinkle them with the dried herbs. Grill for 3–4 minutes, or until golden brown on each side. Remove to a plate and set aside.

● Spray a saucepan with the low fat cooking spray and stir fry the onion and garlic with a few tablespoons of water, until softened. Add the sage and bay leaf, and then stir in the canned beans, lemon juice, green beans and stock.

● Place the grilled chicken on top of the bean mixture and cover the pan. Leave to steam for 5 minutes until the chicken is cooked through and the green beans tender. Serve scattered with the lemon zest.

Provençal casserole

7 *POINTS* values per recipe

Serves 4

165 calories per serving

Takes 40 minutes

The flavours of the sunny Mediterranean shine through in this satisfying and very easy to prepare dish.

low fat cooking spray
2 red onions, sliced
4 garlic cloves, sliced
1 red pepper, de-seeded and sliced
1 yellow or orange pepper, de-seeded and sliced
500 g (1 lb 2 oz) courgettes, sliced in half lengthways and then into half moons on the diagonal
400 g can of chopped tomatoes
300 ml (1/2 pint) vegetable stock
2 tablespoons tomato purée
400 g can of haricot blanc or flageolet beans, drained and rinsed
a small bunch of rosemary, tough stems removed, leaves and tender stems chopped
a small bunch thyme, tough stems removed, leaves and tender stems chopped
20 olives in brine, drained, rinsed, pitted and chopped
1 teaspoon artificial sweetener
salt and freshly ground black pepper
a small bunch of parsley, chopped, to serve (optional)

● Heat a large flameproof casserole and spray with low fat cooking spray, stir fry the onions for 5 minutes with a few tablespoons of water until softened, and bring to the boil.

● Add all the other ingredients and simmer for 20–30 minutes, or until the vegetables are tender and the tomato sauce is thickened.

● Check the seasoning and serve scattered with the chopped parsley, if using.

Baked cheesey leeks

7 *POINTS* values per recipe

Serves 2

305 calories per serving

Takes 55 minutes

This dish is best made with the young tender leeks at the start of the season, which is early autumn.

low fat cooking spray
6 small leeks, trimmed and slit in half from top to bottom, then washed
2 eggs
100 g (3 1/2 oz) low fat soft cheese
100 g (3 1/2 oz) low fat plain yogurt
25 g (1 oz) rye crispbreads
salt and freshly ground black pepper
a few sprigs of fresh thyme, chopped, to serve (optional)

● Preheat the oven to Gas Mark 4/180°C/fan oven 160°C. Spray a shallow ovenproof dish with the low fat cooking spray. Blanch the leeks by putting them in a saucepan of boiling water for 6–8 minutes, until just tender. Drain and arrange them in the ovenproof casserole dish.

● Meanwhile beat the eggs with the soft cheese and yogurt and some seasoning. Break up the crispbreads by putting them in a plastic bag and pounding them with a rolling pin or do this in a food processor. Pour the cheese sauce over the leeks and scatter with the crispbread crumbs.

● Bake for 35–40 minutes, until the top is crisp and brown and the sauce bubbling. Serve scattered with the thyme, if using.

Storecupboard laundry...

*Rye crispbreads are a good NoCount or low **POINTS** value alternative to bread. Use them in your lunch box, with sandwich ingredients or experiment with more creative ideas – such as replacing breadcrumb bases with the crisp base.*

Chicken and spring vegetable fricassée

17 *POINTS* values per recipe   Serves 4

335 calories per serving

Takes 30 minutes

4 x 150 g (5½ oz) skinless and boneless chicken breasts
250 g (9 oz) low fat soft cheese with garlic and herbs
low fat cooking spray
2 garlic cloves, crushed
200 g (7 oz) baby carrots
200 g (7 oz) button onions
200 g (7 oz) baby turnips, halved or baby sweetcorn, halved
425 ml (¾ pint) vegetable stock
½ medium cauliflower, sliced into small florets
½ medium head of broccoli, sliced into small florets
a small bunch of tarragon or parsley, tough stems removed and
    chopped (optional)
4 tablespoons virtually fat free fromage frais
salt and freshly ground black pepper

● With a sharp knife, make a deep incision into the side of each chicken breast. Push a teaspoon of the soft cheese into each slit. Heat a flameproof casserole dish or large saucepan and spray with the low fat cooking spray, then season. Brown the chicken breasts on both sides and then remove to a plate.
● Spray the pan again and add the garlic, carrots, button onions and turnips or baby sweetcorn and brown them all over for 5 minutes.
● Return the chicken to the casserole and add the stock. Bring to the boil scraping up any stuck on juices from the bottom of the pan with a wooden spatula. Cover and simmer for 10 minutes.
● Add the cauliflower, broccoli, tarragon or parsley, if using, and the remaining soft cheese. Season and cover, and then simmer for a further 5–10 minutes, until the cauliflower is tender and the chicken is cooked through.
● Allow to cool a little and then stir in the fromage frais and serve.

Chicken Kashmiri

13½ *POINTS* values per recipe   Serves 4

270 calories per serving ❄

Takes 25 minutes to prepare, 20 minutes to cook

Meltingly tender and moist chicken pieces in an aromatic and spicy yogurt sauce. Serve with 4 tablespoons cooked rice each for an extra 3 *POINTS* values per serving.

low fat cooking spray
4 x 150 g (5½ oz) skinless and boneless chicken breasts, cubed
200 g (7 oz) small new potatoes, quartered
1 onion, peeled and chopped finely
4 garlic cloves, peeled and crushed
5 cm (2 inch) piece of fresh root ginger, chopped finely
2 cardamom pods, seeds only
½ teaspoons cumin seeds
1 teaspoon ground coriander
1 green chilli, de-seeded and chopped finely (optional)
300 ml (½ pint) chicken stock
100 g (3½ oz) baby spinach, washed
300 g (10½ oz) low fat plain yogurt
a bunch of fresh coriander, chopped
salt and freshly ground black pepper
4 lemon wedges, to serve

● Heat a large non stick frying pan and spray with the low fat cooking spray. Stir fry the chicken for 4 minutes or so until golden on the edges and white all over. Add the potatoes, onion, garlic, ginger, spices and chilli, if using, and fry for a further 4 minutes until they turn golden.
● Add the stock and bring to the boil and cover. Simmer gently for 15 minutes until the chicken is tender, the potatoes cooked through and the sauce thickened.
● Stir in the spinach and check the seasoning. Allow to cool a little and then stir in the yogurt, scatter with coriander and then serve with the lemon wedges.

Pot roast turkey with autumn vegetables

6 POINTS values per recipe

365 calories per serving

Takes 20 minutes to prepare, 1 hour to cook

Serves 4

Pot roasting a turkey breast joint like this guarantees moist and tender meat, and it's wonderfully simple.

low fat cooking spray

1 x 1 kg (2 lb 4 oz) turkey breast joint

1 whole garlic bulb, cut in half horizontally

1 lemon, halved

300 ml (10 fl oz) chicken or vegetable stock

a small bunch of thyme, tough stems removed, tender stems and
    leaves, chopped

2 carrots, peeled and thickly sliced on the diagonal

1 pumpkin or butternut squash, de-seeded, peeled and sliced into
    large chunks

1 medium celeriac, peeled, quartered and cut into smaller chunks

1 large courgette, cut into chunks

salt and freshly ground black pepper

● Preheat the oven to Gas Mark 4/180°C/fan oven 160°C. Heat a large flameproof casserole dish and spray with the low fat cooking spray. Add the joint and brown it all over. Remove to a plate.

● Add the garlic, lemon and stock, half of the thyme and a selection of vegetables, except the courgette, to cover the bottom of the casserole dish. Place the turkey back on top. Season and then cover and roast in the oven for 45 minutes.

● Place the rest of the carrots, pumpkin and celeriac with the remaining thyme in a roasting tray, spray with the cooking spray and season. Roast for 45 minutes below the casserole. After 25 minutes add the courgette to the roasting tray, spraying it with low fat cooking spray. When the vegetables are cooked keep them warm.

● Lift the turkey out of the casserole dish on to a carving board. Cover with foil and allow it to rest. Spoon the vegetables into a serving dish and drain the juices into a serving jug, draining off the fat. Check the seasoning and serve three skinless slices per person.

Bubble and squeak

4½ POINTS values per recipe

215 calories per serving

Takes 35 minutes

Serves 2

Ⓥ

Bubble and squeak makes a great last-minute supper dish. Serve it with dry fried eggs (i.e. eggs fried in a non stick pan with no oil) and a cherry tomato salad enhanced with a finely chopped shallot or red onion and a smattering of balsamic vinegar.

2 large potatoes, about 400 g (14 oz), peeled, chopped and
    cooked, or use leftover boiled potatoes

300 g (10½ oz) Brussels sprouts or cabbage, chopped and boiled
    until soft, or use leftover zero green vegetables

low fat cooking spray

salt and freshly ground black pepper

● Mash the potatoes and mix in the green vegetables with a little seasoning. Heat a non stick frying pan and spray with the low fat cooking spray.

● Tip the potato mixture into the hot pan and squash down with a fish slice until the mixture covers the bottom of the pan and is more or less flat on top.

● Turn the heat to very low and cook for 10–15 minutes. Using the fish slice, turn over the bubble and squeak, which should now be golden brown on the bottom. Squash it down again and cook for a further 10 minutes until golden on the bottom again. Serve.

Food fantastic...

Dark green leafy vegetables, such as the Brussels sprouts and cabbage used in the recipe above, contain Vitamin K. This helps your body to make proteins, one of which helps your blood to clot and stay healthy.

Family favourites

Watching your weight does not mean that you have to eat alone. It is just as important for your family to eat well too, for the health benefits if not the weight management. Family food doesn't have to be high in fat to be tasty. You can create wonderful, traditional dishes such as shepherd's pie and spaghetti bolognese, with all the time-honoured tastes, without adding large amounts of fat.

This chapter explores just how to make the most of those family mealtimes, and shows how to make simply and easily all the family's favourites the healthy way. In fact, these recipes are so good – the rest of the family won't be able to tell the difference. From the much-loved classics such as lasagne or traditional roast chicken to the more recent fast food equivalents, such as pizza and burgers, this chapter is filled with a selection of recipes that all the family are guaranteed to enjoy.

Nut roast with roast garlic and tomato sauce

3½ POINTS VALUE

13½ *POINTS* values per recipe

260 calories per serving

Takes 20 minutes to prepare, 45 minutes to cook

Serves 4

Ⓥ

(uncooked) ❄

You may want to chop up a few courgettes, red onions, peppers and/or cherry tomatoes to roast alongside this to make a complete meal.

2 courgettes, coarsely grated

100 g (3½ oz) mixture of 3 types of nuts e.g. walnuts, almonds, cashews, peanuts, hazelnuts, brazil and macadamia, ground in a food processor or chopped finely

2 garlic cloves, crushed

grated zest of ½ lemon

50 g (1¾ oz) fresh breadcrumbs

400 g can of artichoke hearts in brine, drained, rinsed well and chopped

1 teaspoon dried sage or a small bunch of fresh sage, chopped

1 egg white

1 tablespoon tomato purée

1 tablespoon soy sauce

low fat cooking spray

For the sauce

8 garlic cloves, whole and unpeeled

450 g (1 lb) tomatoes, quartered

1 tablespoon balsamic vinegar

salt and freshly ground black pepper

● Preheat the oven to Gas Mark 6/200°C/fan oven 180°C.

● In a large bowl put all the nut roast ingredients except for the low fat cooking spray, season and mix together well. Tip the mixture into the centre of a large sheet of foil sprayed with the low fat cooking spray and shape into a fat sausage about 25 cm (10 inches) long and 10 cm (4 inches) wide, packing it tightly. Roll the sausage in the foil and place on a baking tray. Roast for 30 minutes and then unwrap the foil and roast for a further 15 minutes, until browned.

● Meanwhile make the sauce. Place the garlic cloves and tomatoes in a baking tray, season and sprinkle with the balsamic vinegar. Roast alongside the nut roast.

● After about 30 minutes, when the tomatoes and garlic are brown on the edges, remove from the oven. Allow to cool for 10 minutes and then pinch the garlic cloves to remove the papery skins. Liquidise the tomatoes and garlic and any juices in the tray and check the seasoning. Slice the roast and serve hot with the sauce.

Food fantastic...

Nuts are packed with healthy monounsaturated fats, so they are very good for you even though they are high in calories and should be eaten in moderation. They are said to help to keep your heart healthy, reduce the risk of diabetes and help to prevent gallstones.

⑦ Cheesey pasta and ham bake

27½ *POINTS* values per recipe   Serves 4

430 calories per serving

Takes 40 minutes

A family favourite which is quick and easy to make and will fill everyone up. Serve with sugar snap peas and grilled tomatoes. Vegetarians would also enjoy this dish, just omit the ham.

200 g (7 oz) pasta shapes
4 medium-thick slices lean ham (weighing approx 150 g (5½ oz) in total, sliced into small pieces
a small bunch of parsley, chopped finely
2 tablespoons polyunsaturated margarine
2 tablespoons plain flour
600 ml (1 pint) skimmed milk
1 tablespoon French mustard
100 g (3½ oz) low fat soft cheese
50 g (1¾ oz) half fat Cheddar cheese, grated
salt and freshly ground black pepper

● Cook the pasta in plenty of boiling water as directed on the packet, but drain it when it is still slightly undercooked. Place it in a large ovenproof dish. Add the ham and parsley.

● Meanwhile make the sauce by melting the margarine in a non stick saucepan. Add the flour and stir together for a minute. Then, gradually add the milk by adding a little bit and then stirring vigorously until it is smoothly combined. Now add some more and continue until you have a smooth sauce.

● Add the mustard, soft cheese and seasoning and stir in. Pour this over the pasta and toss it all together until evenly combined. Sprinkle over the grated cheese and bake in a preheated oven at Gas Mark 6/200°C/fan oven 180°C for 20 minutes, or until golden and bubbling.

④ Bangers and mash with onion gravy

16½ *POINTS* values per recipe   Serves 4

365 calories per serving

Takes 15 minutes to prepare, 30 minutes to cook

A great traditional, heartening meal that all the family love.

low fat cooking spray
4 medium onions, sliced thinly
1 kg (2 lb 4 oz) potatoes, peeled and chopped roughly
8 thin low fat sausages
100 ml (3½ fl oz) skimmed milk
600 ml (1 pint) vegetable stock
1 tablespoon Worcestershire sauce
salt and freshly ground black pepper

● Spray a large saucepan with the low fat cooking spray and then add the onions and stir. Season and cover with a piece of baking parchment and then cover the pan so the onions are sealed. Cook over a very low heat for 30 minutes, or until the onions are soft and starting to brown.

● Meanwhile put the potatoes into a large pan of boiling, lightly salted water and boil for 20–30 minutes, until tender when you insert the point of a knife.

● Meanwhile preheat the oven to Gas Mark 6/200°C/fan oven 180°C and cook the sausages for 25 minutes.

● Drain the potatoes and mash them with the milk and seasoning. Keep warm.

● Finish the gravy by removing the lid and the paper from the onions and adding the stock and Worcestershire sauce. Bring to the boil and simmer on a high heat for a few minutes or until thickened, then serve with the bangers and mash, allowing two sausages per person.

Roast salmon fillets with tangy tomato crust

22 *POINTS* values per recipe   Serves 4

380 calories per serving

Takes 35 minutes

These crisp, tangy fillets are an easy midweek supper. Serve with steamed broccoli.

2 egg whites
1 tablespoon tomato purée
4 x 150 g (5½ oz) salmon fillets
100 g (3½ oz) fresh breadcrumbs
low fat cooking spray
200 g (7 oz) cherry tomatoes, halved
a large bunch of basil or coriander, chopped (optional)
1 teaspoon balsamic vinegar
salt and freshly ground black pepper

- Preheat the oven to Gas Mark 6/200°C/fan oven 180°C.
- Beat the egg whites with the tomato purée and seasoning. Dip the fish fillets in the egg mixture first and then in the breadcrumbs to coat.
- Place the coated fish on a baking tray sprayed with low fat cooking spray and bake for 25 minutes.
- Meanwhile place the cherry tomatoes, basil or coriander, if using, balsamic vinegar, and seasoning in a small saucepan with 50 ml (2 fl oz) warm water and cook over a low heat stirring until the tomatoes start to break down.
- Serve the fish with the sauce spooned over.

Cheesey beanburgers

18 *POINTS* values per recipe   Serves 4

200 calories per serving

Takes 15 minutes

Soft textured with a crunchy coating these burgers will be a favourite with all the family.

2 x 400 g cans of mixed beans, drained and rinsed
6 spring onions, chopped finely
100 g (3½ oz) low fat soft cheese with garlic and herbs
2 slices bread, crumbled in a food processor
salt and freshly ground black pepper
low fat cooking spray
crisp salad leaves to serve

- Place the first five ingredients in a food processor and blend to a rough paste.
- Using your hands, shape the mixture into eight burgers.
- Heat a non stick frying pan and spray with the low fat cooking spray. Fry the burgers in batches of four for 2–3 minutes on each side until hot all the way through, golden and crispy.
- Serve two burgers each with the salad

Storecupboard basics...

Tomato purée is a great product that you should always try to keep in stock. It's made from concentrated tomatoes, adding a great tomato flavour to your dishes.

Meatloaf

3½ POINTS VALUE

15 *POINTS* values per recipe

365 calories per serving

Takes 15 minutes to prepare, 1 hour to cook

Serves 4

❄

A contemporary version of this British classic that's much lower in fat and higher in nutrients and fibre. Serve hot with steamed vegetables or cold with salad. The meat loaf will keep, covered, in the fridge for a few days.

low fat cooking spray
250 g (9 oz) turkey mince
250 g (9 oz) fresh breadcrumbs
1 large onion, grated
2 courgettes, grated
2 carrots, grated
2 tablespoons tomato purée
1 egg, beaten
a small bunch of sage or thyme, chopped reserving a few sprigs or whole leaves for garnish
salt and freshly ground black pepper

● Preheat the oven to Gas Mark 4/180°C/fan oven 160°C. Spray a 1 litre (1¾ pint) loaf tin with the low fat cooking spray and then line with baking parchment.

● Mix together all the ingredients, except the garnish, and pack into the tin. Cover with a piece of foil and bake for 1 hour or until the loaf begins to shrink away from the sides of the tin. Remove the foil for the last 15 minutes to brown the top.

● Serve in slices garnished with the reserved herbs.

Easy pizzas

2½ POINTS VALUE

5 *POINTS* values per recipe

275 calories per serving

Takes 40 minutes

Serves 2

Ⓥ

(freeze pizza bases and sauce separately) ❄

A simple but wholesome and satisfying meal.

low fat cooking spray
1 small onion, chopped
200 g can of chopped tomatoes with herbs
1 tablespoon tomato purée
1 x 23 cm (9 inch) thin and crispy pizza base weighing approx 100 g (3½ oz)
a choice of zero toppings (e.g. mushrooms, sweetcorn, pepper strips, cherry tomatoes, lightly steamed broccoli florets, rocket, baby spinach, thin slices of red onion, capers, gherkins)
fresh herbs such as basil, parsley or oregano for the topping
salt and freshly ground black pepper

● Spray a small saucepan with the low fat cooking spray and fry the onion until soft, adding a little water if necessary to stop it sticking. Add the tomatoes, tomato purée and seasoning.

● Bring to the boil and then simmer on a low heat for 10–15 minutes, until thick. Turn off the heat and allow to cool.

● While the sauce is cooking, preheat the oven to Gas Mark 7/220°C/fan oven 200°C. Spoon the tomato sauce onto the pizza base and spread it out evenly to the edges.

● Decorate the pizzas with the zero toppings of your choice and then bake for 15–20 minutes, until the edges are golden brown and the vegetables are charred.

Time saver...

When you have an easy to multiply up, freezeable recipe like these pizzas try to make up two or three batches at the same time. Portion out and freeze the extra food that you don't need so that you have a quick and easy solution for those times when cooking just seems like too much trouble.

3½ POINTS VALUE — Roast chicken with rosemary and lemon potatoes ✓

13 *POINTS* values per recipe

345 calories per serving

Takes 15 minutes to prepare, 1 hour 15 minutes to cook

Serves 4

A Sunday lunch regular – this roast never fails to please. The potatoes need to be parboiled for around 15–20 minutes before you start.

1 x 1.5 kg (3 lb 5 oz) whole chicken
2 lemons, 1 cut into wedges the other cut in half
a small bunch of rosemary, leaves removed from the stalks
    and chopped
400 g (14 oz) potatoes, cut into wedges and parboiled
low fat cooking spray
300 ml (½ pint) chicken stock
salt and freshly ground black pepper

● Preheat the oven to Gas Mark 6/200°C/fan oven 180°C. Place the chicken in a large roasting tray and season all over. Squeeze the juice from the halved lemon over the skin of the chicken and then place the squeezed lemon 'shells' inside the cavity with half the rosemary.

● Place the lemon wedges and potatoes around the bird. Spray with the low fat cooking spray, season and sprinkle with the remaining rosemary. Roast for 1¼ hours, basting occasionally with any juices in the tray, turning and basting the potatoes too.

● To test if the chicken is cooked stick a skewer or knife into the meatiest portion of one of the thighs. The juices should run clear.

● When cooked, remove the chicken from the roasting tray to a carving board, cover with foil and keep warm while you make the gravy.

● To make the gravy, remove the potatoes and lemon wedges to serving bowls and keep warm. Drain off any excess fat and place the roasting tray on the hob. Heat until the juices boil and then add the stock.

● Scrape up any juices stuck to the tin with a wooden spoon or spatula and boil rapidly for a few minutes until reduced a little. Strain the gravy into a jug and serve with three skinless slices of chicken per person, garnished with the roasted lemon wedges and the roast potatoes.

Food fantastic...

Always remove the skin on the chicken before eating. The white fat under the skin is saturated fat, which you should try to avoid when eating healthily. The less saturated fat you eat the better, as a high intake has been linked with an increased risk of coronary heart disease.

4 POINTS VALUE — Lasagne

15½ *POINTS* values per recipe

335 calories per serving

Takes 15 minutes to prepare, 1 hour to cook

Serves 4

(before final baking) ❄

Lasagne may be a cliché but it's still a firm favourite for most people. This one is made with Mediterranean vegetables and a good dish for vegans if you use a vegan low fat margarine. Serve with a big green salad or Crunchy coleslaw (see page 118).

2 red onions, sliced into thick wedges
4 courgettes, cut into chunky cubes
2 red peppers, de-seeded and sliced into strips
2 yellow peppers, de-seeded and sliced into strips
low fat olive oil cooking spray
1 large white onion, chopped and sliced
2 garlic cloves, crushed
2 x 400 g cans of chopped tomatoes with herbs
a small bunch of fresh basil or parsley, chopped
200 g (7 oz) low fat soft cheese
300 g (10½ oz) very low fat plain yogurt
1 teaspoon French mustard
a pinch of freshly grated nutmeg
8 sheets no pre cooking required lasagne
paprika, to dust
salt and freshly ground black pepper

● Preheat the oven to Gas Mark 7/220°C/fan oven 200°C. Place the red onions, courgettes, and peppers in a large roasting tray. Season and spray with the low fat cooking spray and then roast for 25 minutes, or until the vegetables are softened and charred on the edges.

● Meanwhile, spray a non stick frying pan with the low fat cooking spray and fry the white onion and crushed garlic until softened, adding a few tablespoons of water if they stick. Add the canned tomatoes, herbs and seasoning, and then bring to the boil. Turn down the heat and simmer gently for 20 minutes.

● Meanwhile gently warm the soft cheese, yogurt, mustard and nutmeg together and stir until smooth.

● Layer the roast vegetables, lasagne sheets and tomato sauce twice over in a large ovenproof dish, finishing with a layer of lasagne covered in the cheesey yogurt sauce. Dust with paprika and bake for 25 minutes or until golden and bubbling up at the edges.

Top tip

Low fat cooking sprays are now available in sunflower or olive oil flavours. The olive oil is great to use for savoury dishes, especially Italian ones like this.

Sort your surroundings...

When you go to the effort of making a delicious family meal, such as this lasagne make it into more of an occasion. Turn off the TV and use the time to chat over the day gone by. You'll find that not only will you enjoy the food itself more – you'll feel closer to your loved ones too.

Easy frying pan fish pie

21 *POINTS* values per recipe   Serves 4

399 calories per serving   (before grilling) ❄

Takes 40 minutes

500 g (1 lb 2 oz) floury potatoes, peeled and cut into chunks

500 g (1 lb 2 oz) butternut squash or pumpkin, peeled and cut into chunks

low fat cooking spray

500 g (1 lb 2 oz) cod fillet, skinless, boneless, and cut into large chunks

150 g (5¹/₂ oz) smoked haddock fillet, skinless, boneless, and cut into large chunks

2 leeks, chopped finely

200 g (7 oz) low fat soft cheese

2 teaspoons Dijon mustard

2 tablespoons low fat fromage frais

a small bunch of parsley, chopped finely

100 g (3¹/₂ oz) frozen sweetcorn

salt and freshly ground black pepper

● In a large saucepan put the potatoes and squash or pumpkin on to boil in lightly salted water. Cook for 20 minutes, or until tender. Drain but reserve the cooking water. Mash the two vegetables together and season.

● Meanwhile heat a large non stick frying pan and spray with low fat cooking spray. Fry the cod fillets in batches until golden brown and then remove from the pan and set aside.

● Spray the pan again with low fat cooking spray and then fry the leeks for 5 minutes, until softened, adding a little of the potato cooking water to prevent them from sticking.

● Meanwhile beat together the soft cheese, mustard, fromage frais and parsley with some seasoning.

● Return the fish to the pan with the leeks, gently fold in the sweetcorn and season, then spoon over the cheese sauce. Heat the fish mixture through, but do not boil.

● Preheat the grill. Spoon the potato mixture on top of the fish. Slide the pan under the grill for 5–10 minutes, until the mash is golden and the pie hot through, then serve.

Shepherd's pie

20¹/₂ *POINTS* values per recipe   Serves 4

390 calories per serving   (before final baking or grilling) ❄

Takes 45 minutes

500 g (1 lb 2 oz) potatoes, peeled and diced

500 g (1 lb 2 oz) parsnips, peeled and diced

low fat cooking spray

200 g (7 oz) lean lamb mince

2 large onions, peeled and chopped finely

4 garlic cloves, crushed

4 carrots, peeled and diced finely

4 celery sticks, peeled and diced finely

4 leeks, chopped finely

100 g (3¹/₂ oz) frozen peas

600 ml (1 pint) vegetable stock

2 x 400 g can of chopped tomatoes

1 teaspoon Tabasco sauce

1 teaspoon soy sauce

4 tablespoons skimmed milk

salt and freshly ground black pepper

● Cook the potatoes and the parsnips in a large saucepan of boiling, lightly salted water for 10–15 minutes until tender.

● Meanwhile heat a large frying pan and spray with low fat cooking spray. Stir fry the mince until brown all over then season. Add the onions and garlic for 5 minutes, until softened, adding 2 tablespoons of water if they stick.

● Add the vegetables, stock, tomatoes, Tabasco sauce and soy sauce and bring to the boil. Simmer for 20 minutes on a low heat or until the vegetables are tender and the sauce is thick.

● Preheat the oven to Gas Mark 7/220°C/fan oven 200°C. Drain the potatoes and parsnips and mash with the milk and seasoning.

● Spoon the meat mixture into an ovenproof dish. Top with the mash and grill for 2 minutes or brown in the oven for approximately 15 minutes, until bubbling and golden.

Vegetable chilli

12 *POINTS* values per recipe

170 calories per serving

Takes 10 minutes to prepare, 1 hour to cook

Serves 6

(omit Worcestershire Sauce)

A slight rejigging of the ingredients is all it takes to make this a lower fat, but delicious and satisfying dish.

low fat cooking spray
4 garlic cloves, crushed
2 large onions, chopped finely
1 small red chilli, de-seeded and diced finely or 1 teaspoon dried chilli flakes
400 g (14 oz) carrots, finely diced
400 g (14 oz) courgettes, finely diced
2 teaspoons dried oregano
1 teaspoon paprika
2 bay leaves
1 tablespoon fennel seeds
1 teaspoon ground cinnamon
2 x 400 g cans of chopped tomatoes
2 teaspoons Worcestershire sauce
2 teaspoons soy sauce
2 x 400 g cans of red kidney beans, drained
300 ml (½ pint) vegetable stock
salt and freshly ground black pepper
a small bunch of coriander or parsley, to serve (optional)

● Heat a large saucepan or flameproof casserole dish and spray with the low fat cooking spray. Stir fry the garlic and onions for 5 minutes, or until softened, adding a little water if necessary to stop them sticking. Season and add all the other ingredients apart from the fresh herbs.

● Bring to the boil and then simmer gently, covered, for 1 hour, stirring occasionally. Serve with the fresh coriander or parsley, if using, scattered over the top.

Moussaka

14½ *POINTS* values per recipe

235 calories per serving

Takes 30 minutes to prepare, 45 minutes to cook

Serves 4

(before baking)

A low fat version of this gorgeously filling and satisfying Greek dish that's a taste sensation! Serve with a fresh tomato salad.

4 aubergines, sliced into 1 cm (½ inch) thick rounds
low fat cooking spray
2 onions, peeled and chopped roughly
4 garlic cloves, chopped finely
200 g (7 oz) extra lean beef mince
2 teaspoons Worcestershire sauce
2 x 400 g cans of chopped tomatoes
1½ teaspoons ground cinnamon
a small bunch of parsley, chopped
200 g (7 oz) low fat fromage frais
100 g (3½ oz) low fat soft cheese
1 teaspoon French mustard
1 egg
salt and freshly ground black pepper

● Preheat the oven to Gas Mark 6/200°C/fan oven 180°C and lay the aubergine slices on baking trays. Season and spray with low fat cooking spray and bake for 15–20 minutes until golden and nearly dried out.

● Meanwhile, spray a frying pan with low fat cooking spray and sauté the onions and garlic for 5 minutes, adding a couple of tablespoons of water if they stick. Add the meat and stir to break it up and brown all over.

● Add the Worcestershire sauce, tomatoes, cinnamon, parsley and seasoning. Bring to the boil and then simmer, uncovered for 20 minutes, until thick.

● Meanwhile beat together the fromage frais, soft cheese, mustard and egg in a small bowl.

● In a large ovenproof dish layer the aubergines with the mince mixture and then pour over the cheese sauce. Bake for 45 minutes until the top is bubbling and golden.

Vegetable risotto

12½ *POINTS* values per recipe   Serves 4

325 calories per serving

Takes 15 minutes to prepare, 35 minutes to cook

An easy dish that you can put on and leave to cook while you get on with other things. Guaranteed to fill everyone up and you can vary the vegetables according to your family's taste or what is seasonally available.

low fat cooking spray
2 large onions, chopped finely
4 garlic cloves, crushed
2 courgettes, diced finely
2 red peppers, de-seeded and diced finely
450 g (1 lb) mushrooms, sliced
250 g (9 oz) long grain rice
500 ml (18 fl oz) passata
600 ml (1 pint) vegetable stock
salt and freshly ground black pepper

● Spray a large saucepan with the low fat cooking spray and then stir fry the onions and garlic until softened, adding a little water to prevent them sticking.

● Add the other vegetables and stir fry for a few minutes, until golden. Add all the remaining ingredients, stir together and bring to the boil.

● When boiling, turn down to a low simmer and put the lid on. Leave to cook for 30 minutes or until the rice has absorbed all the water and is tender.

Spaghetti bolognese

18 *POINTS* values per recipe   Serves 4

360 calories per serving   (without spaghetti)

Takes 40 minutes

A delicious, simple and quick recipe for this favourite family meal.

low fat cooking spray
200 g (7 oz) extra lean beef mince
2 medium onions, chopped finely
4 garlic cloves, chopped finely
2 tablespoons soy sauce
2 celery sticks, diced
2 carrots, peeled and diced
4 courgettes, chopped
2 x 400 g cans of chopped tomatoes
1 teaspoon dried oregano or Mediterranean herbs
225 g (8 oz) spaghetti
salt and freshly ground black pepper

● Spray a large frying pan with the low fat cooking spray and put on a medium heat. Fry the mince with some seasoning, breaking up with a wooden spoon or spatula until browned all over. Add the onions and garlic for about 5 minutes, until softened, adding a little water if necessary to stop them sticking.

● Add the soy sauce, celery, carrots, courgettes, tomatoes, herbs and seasoning. Stir and bring to the boil. Turn down the heat and simmer for 30 minutes.

● While the sauce is simmering, cook the spaghetti in plenty of boiling, lightly salted water for 10 minutes or until just cooked. Drain and serve with the sauce.

(3) Traditional fishcakes

11 *POINTS* values per recipe — Serves 4

200 calories per serving — (before cooking) ❄

Takes 15 minutes to prepare, 30 minutes to cook

Homemade fishcakes are a world away from the shop bought variety – and children love them. Serve with mange tout peas.

300 g (10½ oz) potatoes, peeled and chopped roughly
3 leeks, chopped finely
4 x 150 g (5½ oz) cod fillets
1 teaspoon French mustard
a small bunch of parsley or dill
1 tablespoon virtually fat free fromage frais
salt and freshly ground black pepper

● Boil the potatoes in a large saucepan of lightly salted, boiling water for 20 minutes, or until tender. Drain and mash. At the same time steam the leeks in a covered colander or sieve over the potatoes until tender. Preheat the grill.

● Grill the fish for about 5 minutes, until cooked through and then flake into a bowl removing any bones.

● Add the mash, leeks, mustard, seasoning, herbs and fromage frais to the fish and gently fold together. Shape into eight patties using your hands.

● Grill for 3–4 minutes on each side, or until golden brown, crunchy and hot right through. Serve.

Fridge laundry ...

It can be tempting to buy ready made shop bought varieties of fishcakes and fish fingers as a quick and easy family meal. However making your own version like in the recipe above not only tastes better but is a much healthier alternative for all the family – and the extra effort required is minimal.

(3) Tzatziki turkey burgers

11 *POINTS* values per recipe — Serves 4

185 calories per serving — (uncooked burgers) ❄

Takes 30 minutes

Turkey combined with added chilli and fresh coriander make these burgers very tasty. Serve with crisp lettuce, tomato and the minty yogurt sauce.

low fat cooking spray
1 onion, chopped finely
2 garlic cloves, crushed
450 g (1 lb) turkey mince
1 small red chilli, de-seeded and chopped finely
a dash of Tabasco sauce
1 tablespoon soy sauce
a small bunch of coriander, chopped
For the sauce
½ cucumber, halved lengthways, seeds scooped out and diced finely
150 g (5½ oz) 0% fat Greek yogurt
a small handful of mint, chopped
salt and freshly ground black pepper

● Spray a non stick frying pan with the low fat cooking spray and fry the onion and garlic for about 5 minutes, until softened and golden, adding a little water if necessary to stop it sticking.

● Place the turkey mince in a bowl and add the fried onion and garlic, chilli, Tabasco sauce, soy sauce, coriander and seasoning. Shape into eight large patties. Preheat the grill.

● Grill the burgers on a foil lined grill pan for about 5 minutes on each side or until cooked through and golden brown.

● Meanwhile, make the sauce by mixing together the cucumber, Greek yogurt, mint and seasoning. Serve the burgers with the sauce.

(6) Pork roast with ratatouille

23½ *POINTS* values per recipe

315 calories per serving

Takes 20 minutes to prepare, 1 hour to cook, plus resting

Serves 4

1 kg (2 lb 4 oz) boneless shoulder joint of pork, fat removed

450 g (1 lb) vine-ripened tomatoes, quartered or halved
    depending on size

2 red onions, cut into wedges

1 red pepper and 1 yellow or orange pepper, de-seeded and cut
    into wedges

4 garlic cloves, unpeeled

2 large courgettes, halved lengthways and cut into chunks

2 dessert apples, cored and cut into thick wedges

a few sprigs of rosemary or thyme

4 tablespoons soy sauce

200 ml (7 fl oz) vegetable stock

2 tablespoons Dijon mustard

150 g (5½ oz) virtually fat free fromage frais

salt and freshly ground black pepper

● Preheat the oven to Gas Mark 4/180°C/fan oven 160°C. Sprinkle salt and pepper all over the skin of the pork and rub in.

● Place all the vegetables and the apple and herbs in a large baking tray, sprinkle with the soy sauce and seasoning and toss together.

● Place the pork joint on top of the vegetables and roast for 30 minutes. Toss the vegetables around, turn the pork and roast for another 30 minutes.

● Remove from the oven and place the pork on a carving board, covered with a piece of foil for 10 minutes, to allow to rest. Pour any fat off the vegetables, placing them in a serving bowl; keep them warm.

● Place the roasting tray on the hob. Add the vegetable stock and bring to the boil, scraping up stuck on juices with a wooden spoon.

● Add the mustard and stir in then remove from the heat and stir in the fromage frais. Serve the sauce with the ratatouille and carved meat; serving 2 slices per person.

(9) Tandoori lamb with warm rice salad

36 *POINTS* values per recipe

380 calories per serving

Takes 20 minutes plus marinating

Serves 4

The lamb in this recipe could be cooked on a barbecue for that unique, smoky flavour.

300 g (10½ oz) low fat plain yogurt

2 garlic cloves, crushed

2.5 cm (1 inch) piece of fresh root ginger, grated finely

2 teaspoons ground turmeric

2 teaspoons garam masala

2 teaspoons ground coriander

400 g (14 oz) lean lamb fillets

200 g (7 oz) rice

juice of 1 lemon

a small bunch of coriander, chopped

a small bunch of mint, chopped

a bunch of spring onions, chopped finely

100 g (3½ oz) mixed salad and herb leaves

4 ripe tomatoes, diced

salt and freshly ground black pepper

● Mix together the yogurt, garlic, ginger, turmeric, garam masala and ground coriander and then toss the lamb in this mixture to coat thoroughly. Cover and chill for at least 5 minutes, but overnight is preferable.

● Cook the rice as instructed on the pack.

● Grill the lamb on a foil lined baking tray for 5–7 minutes on each side, until just cooked through and browned. Allow to rest for a few minutes and then cut into slices to serve.

● Meanwhile drain the cooked rice and mix with the lemon juice, herbs, spring onions, salad leaves, tomatoes and seasoning. Serve warm with the lamb.

Creamy turkey and pepper fricassée

2 POINTS VALUE

8½ *POINTS* values per recipe

Serves 4

150 calories per serving

Takes 25 minutes

Strips of turkey and peppers cooked until meltingly tender and then slathered in a tasty, creamy sauce. Serve with a medium baked potato.

low fat cooking spray
2 garlic cloves, sliced finely
400 g (14 oz) turkey breast fillet, cut into fine strips
4 tablespoons soy sauce
1 chilli, de-seeded and sliced finely (optional)
2 red, yellow or orange peppers, de-seeded and sliced finely
1 tablespoon balsamic vinegar
2 tablespoons low fat fromage frais
a small bunch of coriander or basil, chopped roughly
salt and freshly ground black pepper

● Heat a large non stick frying pan and spray with the low fat cooking spray. Stir fry the garlic for 1 minute.
● Add the turkey to the pan with the soy sauce. Stir fry quickly until browned all over.
● Add the chilli, if using, and peppers to the pan. Stir fry for a couple of minutes on a high heat, until the peppers are browned at the edges and just softening.
● Sprinkle over the balsamic vinegar and then remove from the heat. Allow to cool for a couple of minutes and then add the fromage frais and the herbs and stir through. Check the seasoning and serve.

Turkey and watercress rolls

3 POINTS VALUE

11 *POINTS* values per recipe

Serves 4

175 calories per serving

Takes 30 minutes to prepare, 40 minutes to cook

Attractive little rolls that could be prepared and sliced into three or four pieces to serve as finger food for a party. For lunch or dinner try served with the Green beans with rosemary on page 38.

1 teaspoon cumin seeds
a large bunch of watercress, chopped, reserving some for garnish
150 g (5½ oz) low fat soft cheese with garlic and herbs
finely grated zest and juice of a lemon
4 x 100 g (3½ oz) turkey steaks
low fat cooking spray
300 ml (½ pint) vegetable stock
4 tablespoons virtually fat free fromage frais
salt and freshly ground black pepper

● Preheat the oven to Gas Mark 4/180°C/fan oven 160°C. Heat a large non stick pan and dry fry the cumin seeds until they pop.
● Meanwhile beat together the cumin and watercress (reserving a little to garnish the dish), soft cheese and lemon zest.
● Place the turkey steaks between two sheets of baking parchment, clingfilm or foil and beat with a rolling pin to flatten them out. Slice each steak in half to make eight thin strips and season them.
● Place spoonfuls of the cheese mixture on the turkey strips and spread it. Roll up each strip and fasten with a cocktail stick.
● Spray an ovenproof dish with the low fat cooking spray and place the rolls in it. Pour over the stock and lemon juice. Season and bake for 35 minutes, until the meat is tender.
● Lift the rolls on to serving plates and stir the fromage frais into the juices. Pour the sauce over the turkey rolls and serve garnished with fresh watercress.

Chicken biryani

22 *POINTS* values per recipe   Serves 4

405 calories per serving

Takes 20 minutes to prepare, 1 hour 30 minutes to cook

low fat cooking spray
4 cloves
4 cm (1¹⁄₂ inch) cinnamon stick
2 garlic cloves, peeled
4 cm (1¹⁄₂ inch) piece of fresh root ginger, peeled and finely grated
300 g (10¹⁄₂ oz) brown basmati rice, washed
2 x 150 g (5¹⁄₂ oz) skinless, boneless chicken breasts, cut into bite size pieces
150 g (5¹⁄₂ oz) low fat plain yogurt
¹⁄₂ teaspoon cumin seeds, ground
1 teaspoon ground turmeric
2 onions, peeled and chopped
400 g can of chopped tomatoes
2 teaspoons garam masala
a small bunch of fresh coriander, to serve (optional)
salt and freshly ground black pepper

● Heat a saucepan and spray with the low fat cooking spray and then fry the cloves, cinnamon, garlic and ginger for 1 minute. Add the rice and 850 ml (1¹⁄₂ pints) of water. Bring to the boil and then simmer for 30 minutes, until most of the water has been absorbed. Cover and cook for a further 5 minutes. Turn off the heat.

● Mix the chicken with the yogurt, seasoning, cumin and turmeric and set aside. Heat a large frying pan and spray with the low fat cooking spray. Fry the onions for 4 minutes and then add the tomatoes and garam masala. Bring to boil and simmer for 10 minutes and then add the chicken mixture with 150 ml (¹⁄₄ pint) hot water.

● Bring to the boil and then simmer for 15 minutes, until the sauce is thick and the chicken cooked through.

● Preheat the oven to Gas Mark 6/200°C/fan oven 180°C. Layer the chicken in a deep ovenproof dish with the cooked rice, finishing with a rice layer. Bake for 10 minutes.

● To serve sprinkle with the fresh coriander, if using.

Roast pork chops with apple stuffing

9 *POINTS* values per recipe   Serves 2

410 calories per serving

Takes 15 minutes to prepare, 40 minutes to cook

This recipe is great served with the Braised red cabbage from page 39.

low fat cooking spray
1 large eating apple, grated
2 shallots, chopped finely
2 tablespoons grated horseradish from a jar
1 tablespoon Dijon mustard
4 x 100 g (3¹⁄₂ oz) pork chops
6 tablespoons balsamic vinegar
salt and freshly ground black pepper

● Preheat the oven to Gas Mark 4/180°C/fan oven 160°C and heat a large non stick frying pan. Spray with the low fat cooking spray and stir fry the apple and shallots with a couple of tablespoons of water until softened.

● Remove from the heat and stir in the horseradish and mustard. With a small knife make a pocket in each pork chop by cutting a 4 cm (1¹⁄₂ inch) slit in the side of the meat opposite the bone. Move the knife back and forth inside the meat to make a pocket.

● Push the apple stuffing into the pocket until the chops are plump and rounded. Lay them on a foil lined baking sheet.

● Season the chops and drizzle over the balsamic vinegar. Roast for about 30 minutes or until the chops and stuffing are cooked through.

Food fantastic ...

Do you remember being told that eating carrots would help you to see in the dark? While this is not strictly true, carrots do contain Vitamin A which looks after your eyes, your skin cells and the lining of your nose, throat and lungs.

Light lunches

Lunchtimes can be difficult when you are trying to watch your weight – particularly if you are in the office. Frequently, we make the mistake of thinking that a shop-bought sandwich is a healthy light lunch. However, these are often filled with lots of fats and additives to make the food last longer.

It's much more straightforward to control your weight if you know exactly what is in the food you eat, and the best way to ensure that is by preparing the food yourself. This chapter pulls together some easy to prepare, tasty lunch dishes that you can take in to work with you, or easily make at lunchtime. From seasonal salads to pâtés and sandwiches, you'll find a wealth of healthy and appetising lunchbox solutions.

Pan bagnat (French sandwich)

19 *POINTS* values per recipe

335 calories per serving

Takes 10 minutes, plus marinating

Serves 4

Ideal for picnics, this is a sandwich made by filling the centre of a whole loaf and then slicing it like a cake.

1 round country style loaf, weighing approx 400 g (14 oz)

2 garlic cloves, crushed

1 teaspoon Dijon mustard

3 tomatoes, sliced thinly

1 avocado, peeled, stoned and sliced

2 spring onions, sliced

1 red pepper, de-seeded and cut into thin strips

1/2 Little Gem lettuce, torn up

a large handful of basil, torn up coarsely

salt and freshly ground pepper

● Slice the loaf in half horizontally, remove about 50 g (1¾ oz) of the soft bread inside each half and discard.

● Scatter the garlic over one of the cut faces of the bread and spread mustard over the other.

● Arrange the salad ingredients and basil on one half of the loaf and then place the other half on top. Wrap the whole loaf in foil or a clean tea towel. Place a weight, such as a bread board, on top and leave for at least 30 minutes before slicing and serving.

Warm broad bean and smoked ham pittas

14½ *POINTS* values per recipe

205 calories per serving

Takes 10 minutes

Serves 4

This summery salad can be served as an accompaniment to fish or meat or stuffed into a pitta pocket as suggested in this recipe.

300 g (10½ oz) broad beans

low fat cooking spray

1 onion, sliced finely

1 red chilli, de-seeded and chopped finely

2 garlic cloves, crushed

1 tablespoon balsamic vinegar

50 g (1¾ oz) smoked ham, cut into small strips

a small bunch of mint, chopped

2 tablespoons virtually fat free fromage frais

salt and freshly ground black pepper

4 pitta breads, to serve

● Cook the broad beans in lightly salted, boiling water for about 5 minutes or until tender. Drain and slip them from their skins.

● Heat a non stick frying pan and spray with the low fat cooking spray then stir fry the onion, chilli and garlic for a few minutes, until softened and golden.

● Remove the pan from the heat and add the balsamic vinegar, ham, beans, mint, fromage frais and seasoning. Warm the pitta breads in the oven or toaster. Spoon the ham and bean mixture into the pittas and serve.

(4) Moroccan stuffed tomatoes

16½ *POINTS* values per recipe — Serves 4

250 calories per serving

Takes 35 minutes

A filling lunch dish which combines couscous with the sweet and tangy, hot and minty flavours of North African cuisine. Serve with the Courgettes with mint on page 46 or the Marinated roast pepper antipasto on page 122

8 beefsteak tomatoes
150 g (5½ oz) couscous
2 teaspoons cumin seeds
low fat cooking spray
2 garlic cloves, crushed
25 g (1 oz) dried apricots, chopped finely
100 g (3½ oz) feta cheese
1 teaspoon Tabasco sauce
a small bunch of mint, chopped
zest and juice of 1 lemon
a small bunch of parsley, chopped finely
salt and freshly ground black pepper

● Preheat the oven to Gas Mark 7/220°C/fan oven 200°C. Slice the tops off the tomatoes and carefully scoop out the flesh to leave a sturdy shell. Chop and reserve the flesh. Place the tomato shells on a baking tray.

● Place the couscous in a bowl and cover with boiling water. Place a plate over the top and leave to steam for 5 minutes.

● Meanwhile heat a non stick frying pan and dry fry the cumin seeds until they pop and become fragrant. Put aside and spray the pan with the low fat cooking spray again. Stir fry the garlic for a few minutes, until golden.

● Add the toasted cumin seeds, garlic and all the other ingredients, including the chopped tomato flesh to the couscous. Mix well and then spoon the mixture into the tomatoes and bake for 20 minutes, until golden and heated through.

(2) Tangy potato salad

13½ *POINTS* values per recipe — Serves 6

140 calories per serving

Takes 20–25 minutes

A lighter, tastier version of the heavy, traditional mayonnaise and salad cream potato salad.

1 kg (2 lb 4 oz) new potatoes, chopped into bite size chunks
10 radishes, sliced
a small bunch of chives, chopped finely
150 g (5½ oz) low fat plain yogurt
1 tablespoon low fat mayonnaise
salt and freshly ground black pepper

● Put the potatoes in a large saucepan with plenty of lightly salted, boiling water and boil them for 15–20 minutes, until tender, then drain.

● Place the potatoes in a large bowl with the other ingredients and mix together. Serve warm or cold.

Fridge laundry...

*An immediate, easy, healthy switch to make is to replace full fat mayonnaise with low fat mayonnaise. On average the lower fat variety has half the calories and saturated fat (and **POINTS** values) of the standard version, and you won't be able to taste the difference.*

Carrot and sunflower seed salad

5½ *POINTS* values per recipe

165 calories per serving

Takes 10 minutes

Serves 4

This fresh, crunchy salad has fragrant Japanese style flavourings and is full of valuable nutrients.

2 tablespoons sunflower seeds
1 tablespoon pumpkin seeds
8 large carrots, grated coarsely
2 tablespoons soy sauce
a bunch of fresh coriander, chopped
2 teaspoons toasted sesame oil
1 tablespoon runny honey
salt and freshly ground black pepper

● Mix all the ingredients together in a large bowl. Check the seasoning and serve.

Food fantastic...

Eating seeds, such as sunflower or pumpkin, as used in the recipe above is a great way to boost your Vitamin E intake, which helps contribute to healthy skin. Seeds are delicious raw, roasted or salted, and can be added to baked items to add great flavour and texture.

Honey and mustard chicken salad

12 *POINTS* values per recipe

228 calories per serving

Takes 30 minutes

Serves 4

500 g (1 lb 2 oz) new potatoes, scrubbed and quartered
200 g (7 oz) asparagus, cut into 2.5 cm (1 inch) lengths
2 x 150 g (5½ oz) skinless and boneless chicken breasts
2 teaspoons runny honey
2 tablespoons wholegrain Dijon mustard
low fat cooking spray
1 garlic clove, crushed
large bunch of watercress
200 g (7 oz) cherry tomatoes, halved
For the dressing
1 tablespoon wholegrain Dijon mustard
2 tablespoons virtually fat free fromage frais
1 teaspoon runny honey
salt and freshly ground black pepper

● Put the potatoes on to boil in plenty of lightly salted water for 15 minutes, or until tender. About 5 minutes before the end of cooking time place the asparagus on top and cover the pan. Drain the cooked asparagus and potatoes together.

● Meanwhile slice the chicken horizontally to make two thin breast fillets. Put in a small bowl with the honey, mustard and seasoning and leave for 10 minutes to marinate. Preheat the grill and line the grill pan with foil.

● Heat a large non stick pan and spray with the low fat cooking spray. Stir fry the garlic for a few seconds then add the potatoes, season and stir fry for 5 minutes, until browned on the edges. Tip into a large serving bowl. Grill the chicken for 4–5 minutes on each side, until cooked through and golden, then slice into strips.

● Place watercress on four serving plates and, in a small bowl mix together the dressing ingredients with 2 tablespoons of water.

● Add the chicken strips, cherry tomatoes and asparagus to the cooked potatoes and pour over the dressing. Gently fold together and then pile on top of the watercress to serve.

Caesar salad with houmous dressing

10½ *POINTS* values per recipe

310 calories per serving

Takes 20 minutes

Serves 2

A delicious variation on the classic Caesar salad.

2 thick slices bread, cut into 2 cm (¾ inch) cubes
1 teaspoon dried oregano or herbes de Provence
low fat cooking spray
1 large Cos lettuce, shredded, washed and spun dry
8 x turkey rashers
25 g (1 oz) Parmesan cheese, grated or shaved with a vegetable peeler

For the dressing

1 tablespoon reduced fat houmous
2 tablespoons very low fat plain yogurt
½ teaspoon smooth Dijon mustard
salt and freshly ground black pepper

- Preheat the oven to Gas Mark 6/200°C/fan oven 180°C and place the bread cubes on a baking sheet. Sprinkle with the herbs and spray with the low fat cooking spray. Bake for 10–15 minutes or until golden, tossing occasionally. Preheat the grill.

- Divide the Cos lettuce between two serving plates or bowls. Grill the turkey rashers. Chop the rashers into small pieces and scatter over the lettuce with the Parmesan cheese and baked croûtons.

- Mix the dressing ingredients together in a small bowl or empty jam jar with 2 tablespoons of water and pour over. Toss together and serve.

Crunchy coleslaw

4 *POINTS* values per recipe

105 calories per serving

Takes 10 minutes

Serves 4

Shop bought coleslaws just can't touch a homemade one for fresh flavour and crisp crunchiness.

½ green cabbage, shredded
½ white or red cabbage, shredded
1 red or white onion, sliced finely
2 large carrots, grated coarsely
½ tablespoon poppy seed, (optional)
3 tablespoons reduced fat mayonnaise
1 tablespoon 0% fat Greek-style natural yogurt
salt and freshly ground black pepper

- Mix all the ingredients together in a large bowl and then serve.

Top tip

You can shred the cabbage really speedily in a food processor, if you have one.

(3 POINTS VALUE) ## Salmon niçoise salad

12 *POINTS* values per recipe   Serves 4

250 calories per serving

Takes 15 minutes to prepare, 20 minutes to cook

Fresh salmon is delicious and pretty in this classic, summer salad.

200 g (7 oz) baby new potatoes
300 g (10½ oz) green beans, topped
2 x 150 g (5½ oz) salmon fillets
4 Little Gem lettuces or Cos lettuce hearts, shredded
250 g (9 oz) cherry tomatoes, halved
8 black olives, stoned and chopped
1 red onion, sliced finely
a bunch of basil, torn up
salt and freshly ground black pepper

For the dressing

zest and juice of a lemon
1 teaspoon dried oregano or herbes de Provence
1 tablespoon Dijon mustard

● In a large saucepan, boil the new potatoes in plenty of lightly salted boiling water, for 15 minutes, until they are tender. About 5 minutes before the end of the cooking time, put the green beans on top of the boiling potatoes and cover the pan to steam the beans. Drain the beans and potatoes together and refresh under cold water.

● Meanwhile, place the salmon fillets, skin side down, on a foil lined grill pan. Preheat the grill. Season and then grill the salmon for 8–10 minutes, until just cooked through and crispy golden on top. Take off the foil leaving the skin behind and flake the fish into large pieces.

● Meanwhile use the lettuce leaves to line four plates or serving bowls. Place the potatoes, beans, tomatoes, olives, onion and basil in a bowl Mix together the dressing ingredients and add it to the bowl. Mix together well with seasoning.

● Pile the dressed salad on top of the lettuce and then scatter with the salmon pieces. Serve.

Food fantastic...

Salmon, as do most other fish, contains many trace minerals, including zinc and copper. The zinc aids the repair of damaged tissue and the copper helps your body to use iron properly.

2 POINTS VALUE   Squash and spinach tortilla ✔

8½ *POINTS* values per recipe   Serves 4

230 calories per serving   Ⓥ

Takes 30 minutes

This dish is utterly delicious. Serve with a crisp salad of mixed leaves and cherry tomatoes with a sprinkling of balsamic vinegar. Tortillas are also good cold in picnics and lunchboxes.

800 g (1 lb 11 oz) butternut squash, peeled, de-seeded and
   diced finely
6 eggs
150 ml (¼ pint) skimmed milk
1 teaspoon Dijon mustard
low fat cooking spray
150 g (5½ oz) baby spinach leaves
salt and freshly ground black pepper

- Boil the squash in a large saucepan of boiling water for 10–15 minutes, until tender, then drain.
- Meanwhile, in a large bowl, beat together the eggs, milk, mustard and seasoning.
- Heat a large (20 cm/8 inch) non stick frying pan and spray with the low fat cooking spray. Then add the squash and stir fry for a few minutes, until it turns golden. Add the spinach and stir fry for a further few minutes, until wilted. Tip the egg mixture into the pan.
- Stir gently together and then cook over the lowest heat, without stirring for 10–12 minutes, or until the bottom is golden and the tortilla nearly set. Preheat the grill.
- Slide the pan under the preheated grill for a few minutes, until the top is golden and puffy and the egg completely set. Cut into four wedges and serve.

Top tip

It is necessary to keep the heat very low so that the bottom of the tortilla does not burn before it is cooked through.

0 POINTS VALUE   Marinated mushroom antipasto ✔

½ *POINTS* values per recipe   Serves 2

40 calories per serving   Ⓥ

Takes 10 minutes to prepare

This flavoursome dish can be served as a starter, accompaniment to a main dish or as a light lunch served with the Marinated roast pepper antipasto page 122

low fat cooking spray
1 garlic clove, crushed
450 g (1 lb) mushrooms, sliced
a few sprigs of rosemary, chopped
zest and juice of half a lemon
1 tablespoon virtually fat free fromage frais
salt and freshly ground black pepper

- Spray a non stick frying pan with the low fat cooking spray. Stir fry the garlic for a few moments, until golden and then add the mushrooms, rosemary and seasoning.
- Stir fry on a high heat until the mushrooms release their juices and then become dry again. Squeeze over the lemon juice and scatter with the zest then remove from the heat and stir in the fromage frais.

Sort your surroundings...

Always try to make your own lunches – it doesn't have to be laborious, as this recipe shows. Shop bought lunches (whether it's a sandwich or a salad) can be deceptively high in fat. Making your own not only means that you will be able to control what you are eating more effectively, but you'll save money too.

Marinated roast pepper antipasto

0 *POINTS* values per recipe

Serves 2

100 calories per serving

Takes 25 minutes

A simple salad that can be eaten as a starter, accompaniment or with other salads from this chapter to make up a meal.

2 red peppers, halved and de-seeded
2 yellow or orange peppers, halved and de-seeded
low fat cooking spray
4 garlic cloves, sliced thinly
1 teaspoon balsamic vinegar
a small bunch of basil, torn up
salt and freshly ground black pepper

● Preheat the oven to Gas Mark 7/220°C/fan oven 200°C and place the peppers skin side up on a baking sheet. Bake for 20–30 minutes, or until charred. Wrap them in a plastic bag and leave until cool enough to handle.

● Meanwhile heat a non stick frying pan and spray with the low fat cooking spray. Fry the garlic slices for a few seconds until golden.

● Peel the skin from the peppers and slice the flesh. Place in a serving bowl with any cooking juices in the tray, the garlic, balsamic vinegar, basil and seasoning. Toss together and serve.

Food fantastic...

Peppers contain antioxidants, which studies suggest help to protect against heart disease, strokes and some cancers.

Primavera pasta salad

13 *POINTS* values per recipe

Serves 4

285 calories per serving

Takes 25 minutes

A zestful salad, packed full of vital spring vegetables with gutsy flavours and stimulating textures.

250 g (9 oz) pasta ribbons
150 g (5½ oz) mange tout peas
150 g (5½ oz) baby carrots, trimmed
200 g (7 oz) baby sweetcorn
150 g (5½ oz) broccoli, chopped into small florets
4 spring onions, sliced
For the dressing
juice and zest of 1 lemon
3 tablespoons virtually fat free fromage frais
a small bunch of fresh basil, chopped finely
a small bunch of fresh parsley or chervil, chopped finely
salt and freshly ground black pepper

● Bring two large saucepans of water to the boil. In one pan cook the pasta for 10–15 minutes, until cooked al dente and in the other blanch the mange tout, carrots, baby sweetcorn and broccoli for 3–5 minutes, until they are also cooked al dente. Drain the pasta and vegetables and place in a large bowl together.

● Meanwhile stir the dressing ingredients together in a small bowl. Add it to the pasta and vegetable mixture with the spring onions. Toss together, check the seasoning and then serve warm.

Top tip

This salad can be served warm or cold but it is best warm as the herbs are more aromatic and the vegetables freshest.

Caribbean salsa salad

9½ *POINTS* values per recipe   Serves 4

170 calories per serving   (omit Worcestershire sauce) Ⓨ

Takes 20 minutes plus chilling

A fresh, exciting salad. Great on its own or as an accompaniment to a piece of grilled chicken or fish.

400 g can of red kidney beans, drained and rinsed

½ cucumber, diced

300 g can of sweetcorn, drained and rinsed

250 g (9 oz) cherry tomatoes, quartered

4 spring onions, chopped

2 red peppers, de-seeded and chopped

a small bunch of coriander, chopped

For the dressing

1 garlic clove, crushed

zest and juice of 1 lime

1 teaspoon Tabasco sauce

3 tablespoons red wine vinegar

½ teaspoon Worcestershire sauce

½ teaspoon ground cumin

salt and freshly ground black pepper

● Whisk the dressing ingredients together in a small bowl or shake together in an empty jam jar.

● Mix all the salsa ingredients together and then toss in the dressing. This salad is best left for at least 30 minutes in the fridge for the flavours to infuse, but it can be served immediately.

Roasted tomato and bean salad

6 *POINTS* values per recipe   Serves 4

100 calories per serving   Ⓨ

Takes 15 minutes

A quick and simple salad with vibrant, sunshine flavours. Serve with a special piece of very fresh grilled fish like a Dover or lemon sole.

300 g (10½ oz) cherry tomatoes, halved

low fat cooking spray

2 tablespoons balsamic vinegar

1 tablespoon soy sauce

400 g can of red kidney beans beans, drained and rinsed

2 shallots or a small red onion, peeled and chopped finely

1 garlic clove, crushed

zest and juice of 1 lemon

a pinch of dried chilli flakes (optional)

a small bunch of parsley or basil, chopped

salt and freshly ground black pepper

● Preheat the oven to Gas Mark 8/230°C/fan oven 210°C and place the tomato halves on a roasting tray. Season, spray with the low fat cooking spray and sprinkle with the balsamic vinegar and soy sauce. Toss together and roast for 15 minutes, until golden.

● Meanwhile place the beans and all the other ingredients in a large mixing bowl. Add the roasted tomatoes and gently fold together.

Sort your surroundings...

Subtle changes in your usual eating habits can make a big difference to the way that you feel. Making gradual adjustments like reducing the amount of processed foods you eat, or drinking more water will help you to start feeling happier, more alert and vibrant.

(2½ POINTS VALUE) Mediterranean couscous salad

10½ *POINTS* values per recipe   Serves 4
160 calories per serving
Takes 15 minutes

This salad makes a great pick-me-up lunch full of healthy veggies to fill you up and give you vitality.

200 g (7 oz) couscous
½ cucumber, chopped finely
a small bunch of fresh parsley or basil, chopped
a bunch of spring onions, chopped finely
1 red pepper, de-seeded and chopped finely
100 g (3½ oz) cherry tomatoes, quartered
salt and freshly ground black pepper
For the dressing
2 tablespoons soy sauce
juice of 1 lemon
1 tablespoon tomato purée
½ teaspoon Tabasco sauce (optional)

● Place the couscous in a large bowl and cover with boiling water. Cover the bowl and leave to steam for 10 minutes and then fluff up with a fork.
● Meanwhile prepare all the other salad ingredients and mix together the dressing ingredients in a small bowl.
● When ready, mix everything together and then serve or keep, covered, in the fridge for up to two days.

(4½ POINTS VALUE) Warm rice and peas with ham

9 *POINTS* values per recipe   Serves 2
235 calories per serving
Takes 25 minutes

A hearty dish great to make all year round for a tasty lunch or light supper dish. The very simple tangy dressing can be used in its own right on salads or as a sauce for grilled meat, fish or steamed vegetables like broccoli or green beans.

100 g (3½ oz) brown basmati rice
100 g (3½ oz) peas, fresh or frozen and defrosted
50 g (1¾ oz) lean ham, cut into small pieces
2 spring onions, chopped finely
a small bunch of fresh dill, mint or parsley, chopped
For the very simple tangy dressing
2 teaspoons balsamic vinegar
2 tablespoons low fat fromage frais
salt and freshly ground black pepper

● Cook the rice as directed on the pack for 20 minutes or so, until tender. Add the peas to the rice. Cover and cook for a further 2 minutes or until the peas are just cooked.
● Drain the rice and peas and add all the other ingredients, including the dressing ingredients. Toss together and serve.

Storecupboard basics...

Couscous is a fabulous staple for healthy eaters – so try to keep a stash at home. Traditionally a North African dish, it's made from a semolina base and has a wonderful light, fluffy texture. It can be made up in less than 15 minutes and works as a great base for a filling lunch, an accompaniment or salad.

Chicken and couscous salad

9 *POINTS* values per recipe	Serves 2
300 calories per serving	
Takes 30 minutes	

This substantial salad is served with a delicious minted yogurt dressing that can be used to liven up any salad vegetables or steamed greens.

2 courgettes, halved and sliced thinly, lengthways
1 red pepper, de-seeded and sliced into wedges
150 g (5¹/2 oz) chicken breast fillet, all fat and skin removed, sliced into thin strips
low fat cooking spray
100 g (3¹/2 oz) couscous
100 g (3¹/2 oz) cherry tomatoes, halved
zest and juice of ¹/2 a lemon
salt and freshly ground black pepper
For the minted yogurt dressing
150 g (5¹/2 oz) carton low fat plain yogurt
juice of half a small lemon
a small bunch of fresh mint, chopped finely
salt and freshly ground black pepper

● Line a grill pan with foil and then spread the courgettes, pepper and chicken strips out over it. (You may have to do this in two or three batches depending on the size of your grill pan.)
● Spray with the low fat cooking spray, season then grill for 3–4 minutes. Turn over and grill for a further 3–4 minutes, until the chicken is cooked through and golden.
● Place the couscous in a large bowl and cover with boiling water. Cover with a lid or plate and leave to steam for 10 minutes then fluff up with a fork.
● Add the grilled vegetables, chicken, tomatoes, lemon zest and juice and seasoning to the couscous and toss together.
● Mix the dressing ingredients together then drizzle over the salad and serve.

Smoked mackerel pâté

20 *POINTS* values per recipe	Serves 6
145 calories per serving	
Takes 20 minutes	

A robustly flavoured, creamy textured fresh pâté that is delicious served with crispbreads.

275 g (9¹/2 oz) smoked mackerel fillets
2 tablespoons horseradish sauce
2 tablespoons virtually fat free fromage frais
freshly ground black pepper
6 wedges of lemon, to serve

● Remove the skin from the mackerel fillets and flake the fish into a bowl, removing any bones that you find.
● Add the horseradish, fromage frais and freshly ground black pepper and stir together. Pack into ramekins and serve with lemon wedges. This pâté keeps in the fridge for up to three days.

Just for one

There may be times when you are home alone, or eating at a different time to the rest of the family. If you are cooking for yourself, you are less likely to want to spend a lot of time creating complicated, fussy meals. However, it's important that you still take the time to enjoy the food that you eat.

This chapter shows you how you can really make the most of the time that you have for yourself and the food that you eat. The recipes offer delicious, uncomplicated meals that are quick and easy to prepare, allowing you to savour your food and enjoy your time alone.

Baked chilli eggs (page 135)

(2 POINTS VALUE) Courgette pancakes with spicy relish

2 *POINTS* values per recipe
230 calories per serving
Takes 20 minutes

Serves 1
(omit Worcestershire sauce)

Delicious little courgette cakes to dip into a fiery and spicy relish.

2 tablespoons plain flour
2 tablespoons skimmed milk
2 courgettes, grated coarsely
1 egg white
low fat cooking spray
salt and freshly ground black pepper
For the spicy relish
150 g (5¹/2 oz) cherry tomatoes, quartered
¹/2 red onion, chopped finely
1 small red chilli, de-seeded and chopped finely
juice of 1 lemon
a dash of Tabasco sauce
a dash of Worcestershire sauce
a small bunch of coriander, basil, parsley or mint, chopped finely

● Put the flour and seasoning into a bowl and stir in the milk. Then add the courgettes and mix together.
● Make the relish by mixing all the ingredients together in a bowl.
● Beat the egg white until stiff, and then gently fold it into the courgette mix with a large metal spoon. Heat a large frying pan and spray with the low fat cooking spray. Drop tablespoonfuls of the courgette mixture into the pan (the mixture makes four pancakes).
● Sauté the pancakes for 3–4 minutes, then flip over with a palette knife and cook the other side for 3–4 minutes, until golden brown. Put the pancakes on a plate and serve with the relish.

(3 POINTS VALUE) Warm spinach, turkey and poached egg salad

3 *POINTS* values per recipe
215 calories per serving
Takes 10 minutes

Serves 1

A classic combination that's still very special. The fresh green spinach leaves are perfectly complemented by bursts of crisp, turkey rashers and the warm egg yolk adds richness to the dressing.

1 tablespoon white wine or malt vinegar
100 g (3¹/2 oz) baby spinach, washed and drained
1 teaspoon balsamic vinegar
1 teaspoon walnut, hazelnut or sesame oil
1 egg
2 turkey rashers
salt and freshly ground black pepper

● Put a saucepan of water on to boil with the white wine or malt vinegar in it.
● Put the spinach in a bowl with the balsamic vinegar, oil and seasoning and toss together. Place in a serving bowl or on a plate.
● When the water is at a rolling boil, crack the egg into a small cup and then, holding the cup as near as possible to the top of the water, gently tip the egg into the water from the cup. Cook for 3 minutes then lift the egg out with a slotted spoon.
● Meanwhile, preheat the grill and grill the turkey rashers for 1 minute on each side, until starting to turn crisp. Chop into pieces and scatter over the salad leaves. Top with the poached egg and lots of freshly ground black pepper.

POINTS
VALUE®

Red pepper and sweetcorn fritters

5½ POINTS values per recipe

370 calories per serving

cook with Takes 30 minutes

Serves 1

Ⓨ

These little pancakes are great with a fresh tomato salsa made with a seasoned medley of chopped tomato, finely diced red onion, fresh herbs and a drizzle of balsamic vinegar.

2 tablespoons plain flour
1 egg, separated
2 tablespoons skimmed milk
a pinch of salt
1/2 red pepper, de-seeded and chopped finely
200 g can of sweetcorn, drained
low fat cooking spray

● Put the flour, egg yolk and milk with a pinch of salt in a bowl and mix thoroughly.

● Stir in the pepper and sweetcorn. Whisk the egg white until stiff and fluffy and then gently fold it into the sweetcorn mix with a large metal spoon.

● Heat a large, non stick frying pan and spray with the low fat cooking spray, and then carefully add tablespoons of the batter to make small, drop scone-like pancakes.

● Cook two to three fritters at the same time, for 2–4 minutes, and then flip them over with a palette knife or fish slice and cook the other side for 2–4 minutes, until golden brown. Put them on a plate (the mixture makes four fritters) and keep warm while you cook the others.

Oven roasted tomatoes with goat's cheese

5 POINTS values per recipe

170 calories per serving

Takes 10 minutes

Serves 1

Ⓨ

This delicious lunch or supper dish is best squashed on to crusty bread with a fresh green salad of rocket or another peppery leaf like watercress. Don't forget to add the **POINTS** values for the bread.

100 g (3½ oz) vine-ripened, still on the vine, small tomatoes
1 x 50 g (1¾ oz) small 'crotin' goat's cheese
2 teaspoons balsamic vinegar
salt and freshly ground black pepper

● Preheat the oven to Gas Mark 7/220°C/fan oven 200°C and place the tomatoes and goat's cheese on a non stick baking tray. Roast for 5–10 minutes, until the cheese is softened and golden and the tomatoes beginning to soften.

● Place the cheese and tomatoes on a serving plate and drizzle with the balsamic vinegar. Season and serve.

Time saver ...

When you are cooking for one, opt for something quick and easy such as this recipe. It feels special but doesn't take too long – leaving you more time to pamper yourself.

POINTS
VALUE

(5) Smoked salmon pitta pizza

5 POINTS values per recipe
235 calories per serving
Takes 15 minutes

Serves 1

A quick and satisfying lunch or supper.

1 pitta bread
2 teaspoons low fat soft cheese with garlic and herbs
50 g (1¾ oz) sliced smoked salmon
¼ red onion, sliced finely
1 teaspoon baby capers, drained and rinsed
a handful of rocket leaves
freshly ground black pepper
1 lemon wedge, to serve

● Preheat the oven to Gas Mark 4/180°C/fan oven 160°C. Spread the pitta with the soft cheese. Top with salmon slices and scatter with red onion and capers.
● Bake for 10–15 minutes, until the edges of the pitta bread are crispy. Garnish with the rocket leaves and black pepper. Serve with a lemon wedge to squeeze over.

(6½) Cashew and watercress pilau

6½ POINTS values per recipe
505 calories per serving
Takes 55 minutes

Serves 1 Ⓨ

A satisfying and comforting meal that's also full of the 'good-for-you' factor!

low fat cooking spray
3 spring onions, chopped
1 garlic clove, chopped
75 g (2¾ oz) brown basmati rice, washed
¼ cauliflower, chopped into small florets
juice of half a lemon
¼ teaspoon Chinese five spice powder
100 ml (3½ fl oz) vegetable stock
a small bunch of mint, chopped
a small bunch of parsley, chopped
100 g (3½ oz) watercress, chopped
25 g (1 oz) cashew nuts, toasted and chopped
salt and freshly ground black pepper

● Heat a large saucepan and spray with the low fat cooking spray. Stir fry the spring onions and garlic for a few minutes. Add all the other ingredients except the watercress and cashew nuts and stir together. Cover the pan and simmer for 35 minutes without lifting the lid.
● Stir in the watercress and cashew nuts, season and serve.

Fridge laundry...

*Salad leaves are a great way to add interest and bulk to your meals, without adding any **POINTS** values. Try to vary the salad leaves you buy, until you find ones you like. Rocket, as used in this recipe, has a nutty, peppery flavour that works well with cheese or fish.*

2½ POINTS VALUE **Baked chilli eggs** ✓

2½ *POINTS* values per recipe   Serves 1

250 calories per serving

Takes 40 minutes

An easy supper dish for one that can be rustled up with the minimum of effort, but looks very attractive and feels like a 'proper meal'. Serve with a big green salad of interesting fresh leaves like rocket, watercress, mizuna or lambs lettuce.

low fat cooking spray
1 shallot or small onion, chopped finely
1 garlic clove, crushed
200 g can of chopped tomatoes
1 small chilli, de-seeded and chopped finely
1 teaspoon Worcestershire sauce
1 teaspoon soy sauce or tamari sauce
½ red pepper, de-seeded and diced finely
1 egg
4–5 asparagus spears, woody ends broken off, spears chopped
  but tops left whole
50 g (1¾ oz) lean ham, sliced into small strips
freshly ground black pepper

● Heat a small saucepan and spray with the low fat cooking spray. Stir fry the shallot or onion and garlic for a few minutes, until softened, adding a little water if they start to stick.

● Add the tomatoes, chilli, Worcestershire sauce, soy or tamari sauce, seasoning and red pepper, stir together, bring to the boil and then simmer for 5 minutes, until reduced a little and thick.

● Tip the mixture into a small shallow ovenproof dish. Preheat the oven to Gas Mark 7/220°C/fan oven 200°C. Make a well in the centre of the sauce and break the egg into it.

● Scatter the asparagus and ham around on top of the sauce, season with pepper and bake for 15–20 minutes, until the egg is set.

 2½ POINTS VALUE **Herb crusted baked chicken breast** ✓

2½ *POINTS* values per recipe   Serves 1

165 calories per serving

Takes 30 minutes

Another supremely quick and easy dinner idea. Serve with a baked potato and steamed spring greens, cabbage or broccoli with a drizzle of soy sauce.

1 x 150 g (5½ oz) skinless and boneless chicken breast fillet
a few sprigs of parsley, basil or mint
a few sprigs of thyme or rosemary
low fat cooking spray
250 ml (9 fl oz) vegetable or chicken stock
salt and freshly ground black pepper

● Preheat the oven to Gas Mark 6/200°C/fan oven 180°C. Make shallow cuts into the chicken with the tip of a sharp knife and place on a non stick baking tray.

● Mix the herbs and seasoning together in a small bowl and then spread this over the chicken and spray with the low fat cooking spray. Pour the stock into the tray around the chicken.

● Bake for 20 minutes, until just cooked through and golden then serve with any juices left in the baking tray poured over.

Time saver...

The serving suggestion for this recipe is a baked potato. If you don't have the time to bake your potato in the oven, then just pop the potato into the microwave on a high heat for 7–8 minutes until soft in the middle.

Roast garlic and bean dip

(3½ POINTS VALUE)

3½ POINTS values per recipe   Serves 1

145 calories per serving

Takes 25 minutes to prepare

A quick and easy dip to prepare, with a lovely smooth and earthy flavour. Serve with crudités like carrot or celery sticks and a grated carrot and lemon juice salad for a Middle Eastern feel.

1 small head of garlic
400 g can of cooked mixed beans, drained and rinsed
juice of half a lemon
a pinch of cayenne pepper
a small bunch of fresh parsley, coriander or basil (optional)
salt and freshly ground black pepper

● Preheat the oven to Gas Mark 7/220°C/fan oven 200°C and bake the garlic head on a baking tray for 20 minutes or until soft inside. Remove and leave until cool enough to handle.

● Place the beans in a food processor with the lemon juice, cayenne pepper, fresh herbs, if using, and seasoning. Squeeze the garlic from its skin into the mixture and then blend until smooth. Taste and add more seasoning or lemon juice, if necessary, before eating.

● Eat half and keep the other half for the next day. This dip will keep covered in the fridge for up to 3 days.

Top tip

This recipe makes a double quantity as you cannot buy smaller cans of beans. So reserve one half for the next day.

Storecupboard basics...

Garlic is indispensable in cooking – so always try to keep some bulbs in the fridge. Choose fresh, plump looking garlic with a white skin and a fat neck as these will have a more delicate flavour. Stick to the specified amount in recipes until you know your tastes well – too much garlic will quickly overpower the other flavours in the dish.

Thai chicken salad

(4 POINTS VALUE)

4 POINTS values per recipe   Serves 1

230 calories per serving

Takes 15 minutes

A quick and easy salad to make, with lovely unusual flavours.

50 g (1¾ oz) dried glass noodles, soaked and drained
low fat cooking spray
1 cm (½ inch) piece of fresh root ginger, peeled and grated
100 g (3½ oz) chicken breast fillet, sliced into thin strips
1 tablespoon light soy sauce
2 spring onions, sliced finely
½ green pepper, de-seeded and chopped finely
½ red pepper, de-seeded and chopped finely
juice of 1 lime
1 small green chilli, de-seeded and cored, chopped finely (optional)
a small bunch of fresh coriander or basil, chopped

● Cook the noodles in boiling water for 3–4 minutes, and then drain and rinse them under cold water to prevent them from cooking further.

● Put them in a large bowl and snip them with scissors to make smaller lengths.

● Spray a non stick frying pan with the low fat cooking spray and fry the ginger for a few seconds. Add the chicken and stir fry for 5 minutes, until it is cooked through and golden.

● Add the soy sauce and stir fry a further 30 seconds then pour everything in the pan over the noodles in the bowl. Add all the other ingredients and toss together. Serve.

Sizzling steak stir fry

2½ *POINTS* values per recipe   Serves 1

285 calories per serving

Takes 25 minutes

Sometimes only steak will do. This recipe will satisfy this need and your appetite. Serve with brown basmati rice or noodles adding the *POINTS* values.

low fat cooking spray
2.5 cm (1 inch) piece of fresh root ginger, grated finely
100 g (3½ oz) lean fillet or sirloin beef steak, all fat removed,
    cut into thin strips
2 tablespoons soy sauce
1 tablespoon tomato purée mixed with 100 ml (3½ fl oz) water
4 spring onions
150 g (5½ oz) mushrooms, sliced
100 g (3½ oz) beansprouts
½ red pepper, de-seeded and sliced finely
a small bunch of coriander, chopped

● Heat a large non stick pan or wok and spray with the low fat cooking spray. Stir fry the ginger for 10 seconds and then add the steak and stir fry for 2 minutes, until it begins to brown.
● Add all the other ingredients and stir fry for five minutes, then serve.

Storecupboard basics...

Opt for lean cuts of meat and always cut the fat off meats before eating – you'll be surprised how quickly you go off the taste of fat, and how quickly the pounds start to fall off you.

Spicy chicken skewers

4½ *POINTS* values per recipe   Serves 1

375 calories per serving

Takes 35 minutes plus marinating

Combine with your favourite summer vegetables for a colourful and flavourful meal. Serve with herby rice or the Mediterranean couscous salad on page 126.

1 tablespoon low fat plain yogurt
2 tablespoons soy sauce
1 garlic clove, crushed
1 teaspoon tomato purée
a few drops of Tabasco sauce
1x 150 g (5½ oz) skinless and boneless chicken breast fillet, all fat
    removed, cut into chunks
4 cherry tomatoes
1 red pepper, de-seeded and cut into chunks
½ red onion, sliced into wedges
4 mushrooms
For the pea 'guacamole'
100 g (3½ oz) fresh or defrosted frozen peas
juice of half a lime
½ small red onion, diced finely
2 tablespoons very low fat plain yogurt
a small bunch of fresh coriander, chopped finely (optional)
salt and freshly ground black pepper

● In a small bowl mix together the yogurt, soy sauce, garlic, tomato purée and Tabasco sauce and then add the chicken and stir to cover. Cover the bowl and leave to marinate for at least 10 minutes, but up to 2 hours, in the fridge.
● Thread the chicken and vegetables on to skewers and cook under a hot grill or over a barbecue for 10–15 minutes, turning regularly, until the vegetables start to char on the edges.
● Meanwhile make the pea guacamole by blending all the ingredients in a food processor until smooth. Serve with the chicken and vegetable skewers.

Festive fare

There are some occasions when it is great to pull out all the stops and create a feast for everyone to enjoy. But getting into the festive spirit doesn't mean that you have to revert to high-fat, over-indulgent foods.

This chapter features some wonderfully luxurious dishes without losing sight of the health element. From Christmas day roast turkey to Shrove Tuesday pancakes, you really can enjoy all the best of the season without piling on the pounds.

Christmas day roast turkey with apples and apricots (page 148)

5½ POINTS VALUE
St George's day beef fillet with horseradish crust

43½ *POINTS* values per recipe   Serves 8

370 calories per serving

Takes 20 minutes to prepare, 1 hour to cook plus resting time

What better way to celebrate our English heritage than roast beef and Yorkshire pudding. A real treat!

1 kg (2 lb 4 oz) lean fillet of beef, in one piece or boned and
   rolled sirloin
150 g (5½ oz) mushrooms, chopped
a bunch of rosemary, chopped finely
4 tablespoons horseradish sauce
200 g (7 oz) fresh breadcrumbs
low fat cooking spray
salt and freshly ground black pepper
For the Yorkshire puddings
100 g (3½ oz) plain flour
1 egg
300 ml (½ pint) skimmed milk
For the gravy
2 teaspoons plain flour
300 ml (½ pint) vegetable stock

● Preheat the oven to Gas Mark 7/220°C/fan oven 200°C. With a sharp knife make a slit along the side of the fillet then open it up to make a pocket. Mix the mushrooms with half the rosemary and seasoning and stuff inside the fillet.

● Season the outside of the fillet and then spread all over with the horseradish sauce. Spread the breadcrumbs on a large plate and roll the fillet in them until they are stuck all over.

● Spray a roasting tin with the low fat cooking spray and place the fillet in it. Cover with a piece of foil.

● Roast the beef on a lower shelf for 30 minutes. Take off the foil and brown for a further 15 minutes for a medium cooked fillet and a further 15 minutes for a well-done fillet. Remove the beef from the oven and place on a carving board, loosely covered with the foil again, to keep warm and allow to rest for 10 minutes before carving.

● For the Yorkshire puddings prepare the batter by mixing the flour with a pinch of salt in a large bowl. Make a well in the middle and crack in the egg, add the milk and 100 ml (3½ fl oz) water. Gradually stir in the flour until you have a smooth batter.

● Put a baking tin or patty tin with 12 individual moulds in the oven, on the top shelf, for 5 minutes, until very hot. Using an oven glove remove the tin from the oven, spray with low fat cooking spray and quickly pour in the batter. Return it to the top shelf and bake for 40 minutes without opening the oven door, until the puddings are risen and golden.

● To make the gravy, pour off any fat in the roasting tin and then set it on the hob. Sprinkle over the flour and mix it in with the juices using a wooden spatula. Add the remaining rosemary and stock and boil rapidly, scraping up any stuck on juices with the spatula. Season and pour into a serving jug.

Storecupboard basics...

Eggs are a versatile, nutritious, high protein food and indispensable in the kitchen. Always bring eggs up to room temperature before using, as a cold egg won't whisk well when making batters (as in this recipe) and the shell will crack if placed in hot water.

St Patrick's Day colcannon cakes with turkey rashers

11 *POINTS* values per recipe   Serves 4

200 calories per serving

Takes 10 minutes

Traditional Irish potato dishes are plentiful and delicious. The feast day of St Patrick, patron saint of Ireland, falls on the 17th March.

500 g (1 lb 2 oz) floury potatoes such as Maris Piper or Red
   Rooster, cut into even size chunks
50 ml (2 fl oz) skimmed milk
low fat cooking spray
1 small green cabbage, shredded
8 turkey rashers
salt and freshly ground black pepper
200 g (7 oz) watercress, to serve
2 tablespoons reduced sugar redcurrant jelly, to serve

● Put the potatoes in a large saucepan of lightly salted water. Bring to the boil and then simmer for 15–20 minutes, until the potatoes are tender. Drain and mash with seasoning and the milk.

● Meanwhile, spray a large saucepan with low fat cooking spray and add the cabbage. Stir fry for a few minutes and then add enough water to cover the bottom of the pan. Put the lid on and allow to steam for 8–10 minutes, until softened.

● Drain and add the cabbage to the potatoes with more seasoning, if necessary and mix together. Leave until cool enough to handle and then, using your hands, shape the colcannon into eight patties. Preheat the grill. Place the cakes under a hot grill to brown for about 3 minutes each side.

● Meanwhile, grill the turkey rashers as directed on the packet. Serve each colcannon cake with a pile of watercress, turkey rashers and the redcurrant jelly.

Shrove Tuesday apple pancakes

11½ *POINTS* values per recipe   Serves 4

215 calories per serving

Takes 20 minutes

These also make a delicious dessert or a very substantial breakfast, perfect for those wintry mornings when it's hard to get out of bed.

175 g (6 oz) plain flour
1 teaspoon baking powder
1/2 teaspoon cinnamon
1/2 teaspoon caster sugar
1 egg
300 ml (1/2 pint) skimmed milk
1 cooking apple, cored and chopped finely
low fat cooking spray

● Place the flour, baking powder, cinnamon and sugar in a large bowl. Make a well in the centre, break in the egg and pour in the milk.

● Gradually stir the wet into the dry ingredients, gathering the flour little by little from the edge, until you have a smooth batter. Stir in the apple.

● Heat a large non stick frying pan and spray with the low fat cooking spray. Pour in enough of the batter to cover the base of the pan and then cook for a few minutes, until golden. Toss or flip over with a palette knife and cook the other side.

● Tip the pancake on to a plate and keep warm while you cook the others. The mixture makes eight pancakes.

(3½ POINTS VALUE) May day spring vegetable cobbler

22 *POINTS* values per recipe

265 calories per serving

Takes 35 minutes to prepare, 25 minutes to cook

Serves 6

low fat cooking spray

a bunch of spring onions, chopped

150 g (5½ oz) low fat soft cheese with garlic and herbs

300 ml (½ pint) vegetable stock

200 g (7 oz) baby carrots, tops trimmed and chopped finely

200 g (7 oz) baby turnips, tops trimmed and chopped finely

200 g (7 oz) frozen petit pois

200 g (7 oz) frozen sweetcorn

200 g (7 oz) sugar snap peas

1 head of broccoli, cut into small florets

For the topping

150 g (5½ oz) self raising flour

1 teaspoon baking powder

a small bunch of fresh parsley or coriander, chopped finely

1 teaspoon dried oregano or herbes de Provence

½ teaspoon dried English mustard powder

40 g (1½ oz) polyunsaturated margarine

100 ml (3½ fl oz) skimmed milk

salt and freshly ground black pepper

● Preheat the oven to Gas Mark 6/200°C/fan oven 180°C. Spray a large flameproof casserole dish with the low fat cooking spray and then stir fry the spring onions, until golden.

● Add the soft cheese and stock and stir until smooth. Add all the vegetables and mix, so that they are covered in the sauce.

● To make the topping, mix the flour, baking powder, fresh and dried herbs, mustard and seasoning together in a bowl. Melt the margarine and then pour into the centre. Add the milk and quickly mix together with a wooden spoon, – don't overmix it.

● Using two dessertspoons, spoon the scone mixture into six mounds or cobbles around the edge of the casserole dish leaving gaps in the middle for the vegetables to show through.

● Bake for 25 minutes, until the top is risen and golden and the sauce is bubbling hot underneath.

(3 POINTS VALUE) Halloween pumpkin and cashew nut stir fry

12 *POINTS* values per recipe

220 calories per serving

Takes 25 minutes

Serves 4

Pumpkin is cheap and plentiful in the autumn, and this recipe really brings out its sweet, satisfying flavour.

low fat cooking spray

a bunch of spring onions, sliced finely

4 garlic cloves, sliced finely

2 teaspoons fresh coriander seeds, crushed

2 teaspoons mustard seeds

1 kg (2 lb 4 oz) pumpkin, peeled and cut into small chunks

4 tablespoons soy sauce

150 ml (¼ pint) fresh orange juice

100 g (3½ oz) unsalted cashew nuts, toasted and chopped

a small bunch of coriander, mint or parsley, chopped

● Heat a large non stick pan or wok and spray with the low fat cooking spray. Stir fry the spring onions, garlic, coriander seeds and mustard seeds for a few minutes, until golden and the mustard seeds begin to pop.

● Add the pumpkin and soy sauce and stir fry for 5 minutes more, until the pumpkin is brown on the edges. Add the orange juice and bring to the boil. Now cover and simmer for 4–10 minutes, until the pumpkin is tender.

● Scatter with the cashew nuts and fresh herbs to serve.

Food fantastic...

Pumpkin has plenty of vitamin A which helps our eyes, skin, nails and hair to stay healthy.

Yule log

11 *POINTS* values per recipe   Serves 8

90 calories per serving

Takes 20 minutes to prepare, 30 minutes to cook plus cooling

A light, roulade like yule log that's utterly delicious – decorate with icing sugar and, of course, the ubiquitous plastic robin or snowman.

low fat cooking spray
8 egg whites
a pinch of cream of tartar
2 x 22 g sachets of Lite Hot chocolate
50 g (1¾ oz) caster sugar
1 teaspoon icing sugar or cocoa powder, for dusting
For the filling
50 g (1¾ oz) white chocolate, broken into pieces
60 g (2 oz) virtually fat free fromage frais
1 tablespoon artificial sweetener

- Preheat the oven to Gas Mark 4/180°C/fan oven 160°C. Spray a 30 cm (12 inch) x 23 cm (9 inch) Swiss roll tin with the low fat cooking spray and line with baking parchment.
- Whisk the egg whites in a bowl with the cream of tartar until they form peaks. Whisk in the hot chocolate powder and caster sugar and then scrape the mixture into the prepared tin, pushing gently up to the edges and into the corners.
- Bake for 30 minutes. Meanwhile place a piece of baking parchment just larger than the Swiss roll tin on a work surface. When the roulade is cooked, turn it out on to the parchment and roll up immediately. Place on a wire rack to cool.
- To make the filling, melt the chocolate over a bowl of barely simmering water. Remove the bowl from the heat to cool.
- Fold the melted chocolate into the fromage frais with the sweetener and then carefully unroll the cool sponge. Spread with the filling and roll up again. Dust with cocoa powder or icing sugar to serve.

Christmas vegetarian roast with cranberry & apple sauce

28 *POINTS* values per recipe   Serves 6

315 calories per serving

Takes 20 minutes to prepare, 1 hour 45 minutes to cook

Many families have at least one vegetarian in their midst so here's the Christmas dinner for them.

175 g (6 oz) brown basmati rice or basmati and wild rice mix
low fat cooking spray
2 garlic cloves, crushed
1 large onion, chopped finely
2 carrots, grated
150 g (5½ oz) mushrooms, chopped
3 tablespoons soy sauce
100 g (3½ oz) fresh breadcrumbs
50 g (1¾ oz) unsalted hazelnuts, chopped
2 eggs, beaten
a small bunch of rosemary or thyme, chopped finely
salt and freshly ground black pepper
For the cranberry and apple sauce
200 g (7 oz) frozen cranberries
300 ml (½ pint) apple juice
2 tablespoons artificial sweetener

- Cook the rice in boiling water for 30–35 minutes, until just tender. Drain well. Meanwhile heat a large saucepan and spray with the low fat cooking spray. Stir fry the garlic and onion for 5 minutes, until golden and softened, adding a little water if they start to stick.
- Add the carrots, mushrooms and soy sauce and remove from the heat. Also stir in the breadcrumbs, nuts, eggs, herbs, cooked rice and seasoning.
- Preheat the oven to Gas Mark 4/180°C/fan oven 160°C. Spray a 900 g (2 lb) loaf tin with the low fat cooking spray. Pack in the mixture and bake for 1–1¼ hours, until firm and golden.
- Make the cranberry sauce by bringing all of the ingredients to the boil in a small saucepan and then simmering for 20–30 minutes, until the cranberries are broken down and the sauce is thick.

4 POINTS VALUE
Christmas day roast turkey with apples and apricots

39½ *POINTS* values per recipe   Serves 10

335 calories per serving

Takes 30 minutes to prepare, 2½ hours to cook

Our feast day of feast days when you can really push the boat out and eat this succulent, golden-roasted turkey with all the trimmings. Serve with roast potatoes and the Braised red cabbage from page 39.

4 kg (9 lb) oven ready turkey, without giblets
low fat cooking spray
1 large onion, chopped finely
4 garlic cloves, crushed
400 g can of apricots in juice, chopped roughly, reserving the juice
100 g (3½ oz) fresh breadcrumbs
a small bunch of sage, chopped
6 Cox apples, cored and cut into eighths
200 ml (7 fl oz) vegetable stock
salt and freshly ground black pepper

- Pull out any fat from inside the turkey. Season inside and out.
- To make the stuffing heat a frying pan and spray with the low fat cooking spray. Stir fry the onion for a few minutes, adding a little water if necessary to stop it sticking, until golden and softened.
- Add the garlic and stir fry 1 minute more, then add half the apricots, 4 tablespoons of their juice, breadcrumbs and sage. Season and stir together. Spoon this mixture into the neck end of the turkey and then truss – (sew up the neck with string or strong cotton).
- Preheat the oven to Gas Mark 6/200°C/fan oven 180°C. Place the turkey on a wire rack in a baking tray, cover with foil and roast for 2 hours.
- Remove the foil and drain off all the fat. Remove the turkey and the rack and add the apples, remaining apricots and juice and the stock to the tray. Replace the rack and turkey on top of the fruit and roast for a final 30 minutes uncovered.

- To check the turkey is cooked insert a skewer into the thickest part of the thigh. If the juices run out clear, not bloody, then the turkey is cooked. Place on a carving board, loosely cover with foil and allow the meat to rest for 10 minutes or so before carving.
- Discard any fat from the juices left in the pan and serve with the roast turkey, cooked apples and apricots. Allow 3 slices (approx 150 g/5½ oz) of turkey per person.

6 Christmas or Easter cake

73 *POINTS* values per recipe

380 calories per serving

Takes 20 minutes to prepare, 2½ hours to cook plus soaking

Serves 12

The light version of this favourite where a few of the ingredients have been changed to give a fabulous tasting, moist fruit cake.

200 g (7 oz) dried mixed fruit

100 g (3½ oz) glacé cherries, halved

100 g (3½ oz) chopped walnuts

juice and finely grated zest of 2 oranges

200 g (7 oz) grated carrot

100 g (3½ oz) no pre soak prunes, chopped

2 teaspoons mixed spice

low fat cooking spray

175 g (6 oz) polyunsaturated margarine

50 g (1¾ oz) soft brown sugar

5 eggs

250 g (9 oz) self raising flour

3–4 tablespoons skimmed milk (optional)

● Mix the first seven ingredients together in a bowl and leave, preferably overnight, to soak.

● Preheat the oven to Gas Mark 2/150°C/fan oven 130°C. Spray a 20 cm (8 inch) round, preferably loose bottomed cake tin with low fat cooking spray and line it with baking parchment.

● Cream the margarine and sugar together until light and fluffy, preferably with an electric whisk. Then beat in the eggs, one at a time.

● Lightly fold the flour into the mixture. Now fold in the fruit mixture and just enough milk, if using, to make a batter just moist enough to drop off the spoon if given a good shake.

● Spoon into the prepared tin and bake for about 2½ hours or until a warm skewer inserted into the middle comes out clean.

● Allow the cake to cool in the tin for an hour before placing on a cooling rack. To store the cake, wrap it in greaseproof paper and then a layer of foil.

Top tips

For the Christmas cake, brush the cooled cake with 1 tablespoon of reduced sugar jam, warmed with 2 tablespoons of water, and then cover it with 100 g (3½ oz) marzipan rolled out into a 1 cm (½ inch) thick circle for the top and a strip to cover the sides. Cover the marzipan with 150 g (5½ oz) ready to roll icing. The *POINTS* values per serving will be 7½.

For the Easter cake, roll 12 balls from 50 g (1¾ oz) of marzipan and arrange the balls on the cake. Put the cake under the grill for a few minutes, watching it very carefully, until the marzipan is very slightly browned. The *POINTS* values per serving will be 6½.

Fridge laundry...

Replace butter, which is high in saturated fat, with polyunsaturated margarine. Polyunsaturated fat provides fatty acids that can help healthy skin and the development of body cells.

St Valentine's day seafood and tomato pasta

6 POINTS VALUE

12 *POINTS* values per recipe
Serves 2

500 calories per serving

Takes 35 minutes

Easy to prepare, using fresh or frozen seafood, this is something special for someone special.

200 g (7 oz) spaghetti or linguini
low fat cooking spray
1 onion, sliced finely
400 g can of chopped tomatoes
2 tablespoons capers, washed and drained
200 g (7 oz) seafood selection e.g. prawns, baby squid, scallops, mussels etc. fresh or frozen and defrosted
1 tablespoon Worcestershire sauce
1–2 drops Tabasco sauce (optional)
a small bunch of fresh parsley, chopped
salt and freshly ground black pepper

● Cook the pasta in plenty of boiling, salted water for about 15 minutes, until just cooked.

● Meanwhile, spray a large frying pan with the low fat cooking spray and fry the onion for 5 minutes, until they are softened, adding a few tablespoons of water if they stick.

● Add the tomatoes, capers and seasoning and stir together. Bring to the boil and then simmer for 10 minutes or until the sauce is thickened.

● Add the seafood, Worcestershire sauce and, Tabasco sauce, if using. Stir in and cook a further 3 minutes. Drain the pasta but reserve about 4 tablespoons of the cooking liquid. Toss the pasta with the sauce and the reserved cooking liquid then sprinkle with the fresh parsley and serve.

Easter Sunday roast lamb with thyme and mint gravy

4½ POINTS VALUE

35 *POINTS* values per recipe
Serves 8

350 calories per serving

Takes 15 minutes to prepare, 1 hour to cook plus resting time

To cook this the Weight Watchers way all the fat that would usually be left on the joint is removed. However, to prevent it from drying out, the joint is covered with a delicious herby, yogurt crust that keeps the meat succulent.

1.5 kg (3 lb 5 oz) leg of lamb, all fat removed
500 g (1 lb 2 oz) 0% fat Greek yogurt
1 teaspoon toasted cumin seeds, crushed in a pestle and mortar
a small bunch of mint, chopped
a small bunch of thyme, stems removed and leaves chopped
200 ml (7 fl oz) vegetable stock
salt and freshly ground black pepper

● Heat the oven to Gas Mark 5/190°C/fan oven 170°C. Rub the meat all over with seasoning and place in a roasting tray.

● Mix the yogurt with the cumin, mint and thyme and smear all over the meat, piling it up on the top. Roast the meat for about 1 hour depending on how much the joint weighs (see Top tip).

● Remove the meat from the oven. Wrap it in foil on a carving board and let it rest for 20 minutes before carving.

● Place the roasting tin on the hob and heat. Add the stock and let it bubble for a few minutes while you scrape up all the baked on juices with a wooden or metal spatula. Strain the gravy through a sieve and into a serving jug. Serve three slices of lamb (100 g/3½ oz) per person.

Top tip

On the bone joints of lamb, such as leg of lamb, need 20 minutes roasting time per 450 g (1 lb). Rolled joints of lamb, i.e. with no bone, need 25 minutes roasting time per 450 g (1 lb). Remove all fat from the joint and wrap in foil until the last 20 minutes when the foil should be removed to allow the joint to crisp.

Guy Fawkes chicken and pepper crackers

14 *POINTS* values per recipe

180 calories per serving

Takes 25 minutes plus marinating

Serves 8

These hot and fiery chicken skewers are great for cooking on the barbecue or under the grill.

16 long bamboo or metal skewers

4 x 150 g (5¹/₂ oz) skinless and boneless chicken breasts, cut into bite size cubes

4 red peppers, de-seeded and cut into thick wedges

2 courgettes, cut on a diagonal into 2.5 cm (1 inch) thick chunks

2 red onions, cut into wedges

2 corns on the cob, cut into 5 cm (2 inch) thick rounds

16, or more, bay leaves

For the marinade

150 g (5¹/₂ oz) low fat plain yogurt

2 red chillies, de-seeded and chopped finely

1 green chilli, de-seeded and chopped finely

juice and zest of 2 limes

6 tablespoons soy sauce

1 teaspoon Tabasco sauce

2 tablespoons Worcestershire sauce

1 teaspoon ground turmeric

2.5 cm (1 inch) piece of fresh root ginger, grated finely

2 garlic cloves, crushed

a small bunch of coriander, chopped

● Mix all the marinade ingredients together in a large, shallow baking dish or oven tray.

● If you are using bamboo skewers soak them in water for 30 minutes before using to prevent them burning. Thread the various bits of meat and vegetables with the bay leaves on to the skewers and then lay them in the marinade, basting to cover the meat.

● Cover and leave to marinate for at least 30 minutes, but overnight in the fridge is best.

● Preheat the grill or barbecue. Cook the skewers for 10 minutes, brushing them liberally with the marinade and turning often, until they are golden and charred at the edges and the chicken is cooked through.

St David's Day leek and mustard potato tart

2½ POINTS VALUE

9½ *POINTS* values per recipe   Serves 4

185 calories per serving   Ⓥ

Takes 25 minutes to prepare, 30 minutes to cook

Flavours and textures combined in a fittingly Welsh dish. Serve hot with steamed vegetables or cold with salad.

450 g (1 lb) potatoes, peeled and cut into pieces
2 large leeks, sliced finely and washed
1 egg
150 ml (¼ pint) skimmed milk
100 g (3½ oz) low fat soft cheese
1 tablespoon Dijon mustard
salt and freshly ground black pepper

● Boil the potatoes and, at the same time, steam the leeks, preferably over the potatoes. Do this in a covered metal colander. Then drain the potatoes well and mash with seasoning.
● Preheat the oven to Gas mark 7/220°C/fan oven 200°C. Line a 20 cm (8 inch) loose bottomed cake tin with non stick baking paper and then pile in the mash and press down to make a base. Bake in the oven for 15 minutes until it has formed a crust.
● Pile the steamed leeks on top of the potato base, season and spread to cover the tart base evenly.
● In a jug beat together the egg, milk, soft cheese and mustard with some seasoning. Pour over the leeks and return to the oven for a further 10–15 minutes, until the tart is set and golden.

Boxing Day turkey hash cake

2½ POINTS VALUE

10½ *POINTS* values per recipe   Serves 4

160 calories per serving

Takes 25 minutes

A great leftovers dish that can be made with any roasted meat and vegetables and served with cranberry sauce or ketchup.

200 g (7 oz) leftover potatoes or boiled potatoes, mashed
200 g (7 oz) cooked Brussels sprouts, cabbage, carrots, chopped roughly
200 g (7 oz) cooked turkey, chopped
1 tablespoon wholegrain mustard
2 tablespoons low fat fromage frais
2 eggs
low fat cooking spray
salt and freshly ground black pepper

● Place all the ingredients, apart from the low fat cooking spray, in a bowl and mix together.
● Spray a large non stick frying pan with the low fat cooking spray and tip the mixture in. Pack it down with the back of a spoon or your hand so that the hash fills the pan. Cook the hash over a very gentle heat for 10–15 minutes, until golden brown on the bottom. Preheat the grill.
● Place the pan under the grill to brown the top of the hash. Slice into four wedges to serve.

Fridge laundry...

Replace whole or semi-skimmed milk with skimmed milk. There is just as much calcium in skimmed milk as there is in either whole or semi-skimmed, so you can rest assured that your bones won't suffer as a result of the change.

Special occasions

Sometimes we all want to create a special something for the people that we love, and often that comes in the form of food – whether it's a romantic meal for two or a birthday treat for friends or family. This is where low fat foods can come into their element – if you really make the most of the wonderful foods and flavours that are available, you can create truly inspiring meals that your loved ones will delight in.

From mussels with tarragon and tiger prawn curry to exotic tagines and succulent steak, this chapter will lead you through some truly special dishes that will charm the senses. Sometimes you simply can't beat the magic of carefully prepared and beautifully presented homecooked food – your friends and family will love it.

Grilled Thai prawns with salsa (page 156)

Grilled Thai prawns with salsa

4 POINTS values per recipe

155 calories per serving

Takes 20 minutes plus marinating

Serves 4

This recipe combines prawns with the vibrant, sun-drenched flavours of Southeast Asia.

2 stems lemongrass, sliced finely

2 garlic cloves, sliced finely

2.5 cm (1 inch) piece of fresh ginger, peeled and grated finely

zest and juice of 2 limes

2 tablespoons fish sauce

1 teaspoon runny honey

20 raw tiger prawns, peeled

8 wooden satay sticks

For the salsa

1 mango, stoned and diced finely

a small bunch of fresh coriander, chopped

1/2 cucumber, sliced in half lengthways and then sliced into thin semi-circles

juice of half a lime

salt and freshly ground black pepper

● Mix the lemongrass, garlic, ginger, zest and juice of the limes, fish sauce and honey together in a bowl and then fold in the prawns. Chill and allow to marinate for at least 30 minutes, but preferably an hour. Soak the satay sticks in water to prevent burning.

● Meanwhile, mix the mango, coriander, cucumber and lime juice together with some seasoning and place in a serving bowl.

● Preheat the grill and cover the grill pan in foil. Thread the prawns on to the satay sticks and then grill the prawns under a high heat for 2 minutes on each side or until pink, spooning over the remaining marinade as they cook. Serve with the salsa.

Top tip

Fish sauce is available from larger supermarkets, Asian shops and some health food stores. It has a strong, pungent odour, but adds a delicious savoury flavour to dishes.

Chickpea and tomato tagine

13 POINTS values per recipe

240 calories per serving

Takes 15 minutes to prepare, 45 minutes to cook

Serves 4

This dish uses the typically North African and Middle Eastern combination of coriander, cumin, cinnamon and apricots. Serve with couscous or rice and plain low fat yogurt.

low fat cooking spray

2 aubergines, diced finely

1 large onion, chopped finely

3 garlic cloves, crushed

300 g (10½ oz) sweet potatoes, peeled and diced finely

1 tablespoon ground cinnamon

1 tablespoon ground coriander

2 teaspoons cumin seeds

2 teaspoons turmeric

400 g can of chopped tomatoes

1 tablespoon tomato purée

2 teaspoons Tabasco sauce

75 g (2¾ oz) dried apricots, chopped

400 g can of chickpeas, drained and rinsed

200 g (7 oz) cherry tomatoes, halved

200 ml (7 fl oz) vegetable stock

a small bunch of fresh mint or coriander, chopped

● Spray a large saucepan with the low fat cooking spray and add the aubergines. Season and stir fry for a few minutes, until golden brown.

● Remove the aubergines to a plate and spray the pan again with the low fat cooking spray. Fry the onion and garlic for a few minutes, until soft and golden, adding a little water if necessary to stop them sticking.

● Return the aubergines to the pan with all the other ingredients apart from the mint or coriander. Bring to the boil and then simmer for 30 minutes, until you have a good rich sauce.

● Stir through the mint or fresh coriander and serve.

Asparagus, pea and mint risotto

15½ *POINTS* values per recipe

295 calories per serving

Takes 35 minutes

Serves 4

Ⓥ

A creamy textured, beautiful green and satisfying supper dish. Accompany with a zero tomato salad drizzled with balsamic vinegar.

500 g (1 lb 2 oz) asparagus
200 g (7 oz) frozen petit pois
low fat cooking spray
1 onion, chopped finely
3 garlic cloves, crushed
225 g (8 oz) risotto rice
150 ml (¼ pint) white wine
1 vegetable stock cube
a small bunch of mint, chopped
salt and freshly ground black pepper

- Cut any thick ends of the asparagus into shorter pieces and leave the thin, tender tips as bigger pieces to ensure even cooking. Place the asparagus and peas on to cook in a saucepan with 1 litre (1¾ pints) boiling water for 5 minutes, or until just tender.
- Meanwhile heat a large, heavy saucepan, spray with the low fat cooking spray and gently stir fry the onion and garlic until softened, adding a little water if necessary to stop them sticking.
- Add the rice and stir well, then add the wine and stir in. Drain the asparagus, but reserve the cooking liquid. Mix the vegetable stock cube in with this reserved cooking liquid, in small quantities, to the rice, stirring frequently, until it has all been absorbed and the rice is just tender.
- Fold in the asparagus, peas and mint. Check the seasoning and serve.

Grilled chicken with grapes

3 POINTS VALUE

11½ *POINTS* values per recipe   Serves 4

205 calories per serving

Takes 25 minutes plus marinating

A slightly unusual but delicious combination of flavours. Accompany this with vegetable dishes like the Courgettes with mint on page 46 or Green beans with rosemary (page 38). Serve with 4 tablespoons of cooked basmati rice for an extra 3 *POINTS* values per portion.

200 ml (7 fl oz) red grape juice
1 small onion or 2 shallots, chopped finely
a small bunch of fresh parsley, chopped finely
juice of 1 lemon
4 x 150 g (5½ oz) skinless, boneless chicken breast fillets
100 g (3½ oz) red grapes, halved
salt and freshly ground black pepper

● Put the grape juice, small onion or shallots, parsley, lemon juice and seasoning in a large bowl and then add the chicken. Stir until it is thoroughly coated in the marinade. Chill and leave to marinate for a minimum of 30 minutes, but preferably overnight.
● Preheat the grill. Take the chicken out of the marinade and grill for 4–8 minutes on each side, until cooked through and golden.
● Meanwhile heat the marinade with the grapes until boiling, and then turn down the heat and simmer for a few minutes to reduce the sauce down a little.
● Serve the chicken with the hot marinade sauce.

Glazed oriental salmon

5½ POINTS VALUE

22½ *POINTS* values per recipe   Serves 4

345 calories per serving

Takes 25 minutes plus marinating

A chic and stylish dinner that tastes as fantastic as it looks.

4 cm (1½ inch) piece of fresh root ginger, chopped finely
4 garlic cloves, chopped finely
75 g (2¾ oz) oyster sauce
1 tablespoon sweet chilli sauce
2 tablespoons soy sauce, plus extra to serve
4 x 150 g (5½ oz) salmon fillets
4 heads of bok choy, halved
4 carrots, sliced into thin matchsticks
a small bunch of coriander, chopped

● In a bowl mix the ginger, garlic, oyster sauce, sweet chilli sauce and soy sauce. Place the salmon in the bowl and cover with the marinade. Refrigerate for at least 15 minutes and up to 1 hour.
● Preheat the oven to Gas Mark 7/220°C/fan oven 200°C and arrange the fish, skin side down, on a baking tray. Pour over the marinade and bake for 15–20 minutes, basting with the marinade every 5 minutes or so, until just cooked through, golden brown and caramelised on the top.
● Meanwhile steam the bok choy and carrots over a pan of boiling water for 2 minutes or until just tender – the carrots should be al dente.
● Toss the bok choy and carrots with the coriander and arrange on four warmed plates. Drizzle with a little soy sauce and then arrange the salmon on top and pour over some of the marinade from the baking tray to serve.

Sort your surroundings...

Opt for healthy cooking methods such as steaming, grilling or poaching rather than frying. The flavour will be just as good, but you won't need to use lots of oil or butter and any excess fat will drain away.

Roast pork fillet with mushroom stuffing

14 POINTS values per recipe Serves 4

250 calories per serving (the stuffed pork fillet before cooking) ❄

Takes 20 minutes to prepare, 25 minutes to cook

A meltingly tender pork roast that would be great for a Sunday lunch or special dinner. Serve with Braised red cabbage on page 39 and Potato wedges on page 44.

200 g (7 oz) mushrooms
a small bunch of thyme, leaves removed from stems and chopped
zest and juice of 1 orange
2 x 300 g (10¹/2 oz) pork tenderloin fillets, trimmed of all fat
2 teaspoons cornflour
300 ml (¹/2 pint) hot vegetable stock
salt and freshly ground black pepper

● Preheat the oven to Gas Mark 7/220°C/fan oven 200°C. Blend the mushrooms, thyme, orange zest and seasoning together in a food processor and then tip into a bowl.
● Lay each fillet on a chopping board and make a deep slit along the length, but don't cut all the way through.
● Season the meat and then fill each fillet with the mushroom mix, packing it down as you go. Secure the fillets back together with cocktail sticks or string and then place in a roasting tin.
● Pour over the orange juice and roast for 20–25 minutes, until cooked through and golden. Remove the pork from the roasting tin and allow to rest on a carving board for a few minutes while you make the gravy.
● Mix the cornflour to a smooth paste with a couple of tablespoons of water. Place the roasting tin on the hob and add the cornflour mixture stirring and scraping any stuck on juices from the bottom of the pan with a slotted spatula. Pour in the stock and bring to the boil. Bubble rapidly for 3–4 minutes, until thickened.
● Season the gravy to taste and then serve with the pork.

Marinated trout fillets with apricot couscous

14 POINTS values per recipe Serves 2

340 calories per serving

Takes 25 minutes plus marinating

The simple marinade used in this recipe can also be rubbed on lamb before grilling or used as a dip for crudités or roast vegetables. A side salad of watercress or rocket with ripe tomatoes, a squeeze of lemon juice and seasoning makes a wonderful accompaniment.

150 g (5¹/2 oz) very low fat plain yogurt
2 cm (³/4 inch) piece of fresh root ginger, peeled and grated finely
2 garlic cloves, crushed
1 small red chilli, de-seeded and chopped finely
1 whole trout (approx 400 g/14 oz filleted)
50 g (1³/4 oz) couscous
100 ml (3¹/2 fl oz) boiling water
25 g (1 oz) dried apricots, chopped finely
a small bunch of parsley, chopped finely
zest and juice of 1 lemon
200 g (7 oz) cherry tomatoes, halved
salt and freshly ground black pepper

● Mix together the yogurt, ginger, garlic, chilli and seasoning and rub it over both sides of the trout fillets. Chill and leave to marinate for at least 30 minutes, but up to 2 hours.
● Preheat the grill. Cook the fish under the hot grill for 4–5 minutes on each side, until golden and cooked through.
● Meanwhile, put the couscous in a bowl and pour over the boiling water. Cover with a plate or other lid so that it will steam for 5 minutes.
● Break up the steamed couscous with a fork and stir through the apricots, parsley, lemon zest, lemon juice and seasoning. Serve the trout on a bed of couscous with the tomatoes on the side.

⑦ Beef and wild mushroom stroganoff

27½ *POINTS* values per recipe   Serves 4

405 calories per serving ❄

Takes 20 minutes

Serve this comforting casserole with a sweet potato mash.

low fat cooking spray
2 x 400 g (14 oz) rump steaks, all fat removed and cut into thin strips
4 shallots, sliced in half lengthways and then into fine semi-circles
4 garlic cloves, crushed
500 g (1 lb 2 oz) wild mushrooms or a combination of wild and
    field or button and chestnut mushrooms
a small bunch of thyme, stalks removed and leaves chopped
2 tablespoons tomato purée
2 tablespoons Dijon mustard
a small bunch of parsley, chopped roughly
200 g (7 oz) half fat crème fraîche
½ teaspoon paprika
salt and freshly ground black pepper

● Heat a large non stick pan and spray with the low fat cooking spray. Fry a handful of the steak pieces, with seasoning, over a high heat until browned all over. Remove to a plate and fry the rest of the meat in batches.

● Spray the pan again with the low fat cooking spray. Fry the shallots and garlic until soft, adding a little water if necessary to stop them sticking.

● Add the mushrooms, thyme, seasoning and the tomato purée and cook, stirring, for 1 minute.

● Put the steak back in the pan with any juices, the mustard and parsley and mix together.

● Stir in the crème fraîche and cook on a low heat for 45 minutes, and then stir in the paprika. Check the seasoning and serve.

Top tip

To make sweet potato mash, peel and chop approximately 300 g (10½ oz) of sweet potatoes. Cook in slightly salted, boiling water for 15–20 minutes until tender. Mash with seasoning. Add 1 *POINTS* value per serving.

④½ Filo vegetable pie

27½ *POINTS* values per recipe   Serves 6

310 calories per serving Ⓥ

Takes 30 minutes to prepare, 40 minutes to cook

An exceptionally beautiful and tasty pie fit for a celebratory meal.

low fat cooking spray
300 g (10½ oz) leeks, sliced
300 g (10½ oz) carrots, cut into 1 cm (½ inch) dice
250 g (9 oz) mushrooms, sliced
250 g (9 oz) Savoy cabbage, shredded
2 cm (¾ inch) piece of fresh root ginger, peeled and chopped finely
300 g (10½ oz) very low fat soft cheese
150 g (5½ oz) low fat plain yogurt
2 eggs, beaten
350 g (12 oz) filo pastry, defrosted
salt and freshly ground black pepper

● Preheat the oven to Gas Mark 4/180°C/fan oven 160°C. Heat a large saucepan and spray with the low fat cooking spray. Stir fry the leeks and carrots for 5 minutes. Add the mushrooms, cabbage and ginger, and cook for a further 2 minutes.

● Turn the vegetable mixture into a bowl and allow it to cool. In another bowl whisk the soft cheese, yogurt and eggs together. Season and pour this over the vegetables.

● Spray the inside of a 20 cm (8 inch) springform cake tin with low fat cooking spray and line with a few sheets of the filo pastry. Spray the filo with the cooking spray and then add more sheets overlapping them to line the base and sides of the tin so that there are no gaps (the sheets will hang over the edge of the tin).

● Spoon in the vegetable mixture. Fold in the filo pastry that is hanging over the edges of the tin so that it covers the vegetables. Spray the remaining sheets of filo with the cooking spray and cut into 2.5 cm (1 inch) strips.

● Cover the surface of the pie with the strips, arranging them decoratively then spray again. Bake for 35–40 minutes until golden brown and crisp all over. Allow to stand for 5 minutes to cool a little. Remove from the tin and serve.

Sweet potato roulade

20 POINTS values per recipe — Serves 6

210 calories per serving

Takes 30 minutes to prepare, 15 minutes to cook

600 g (1 lb 5 oz) sweet potatoes, peeled and chopped roughly
low fat cooking spray
225 g (8 oz) low fat soft cheese with garlic and herbs
5 tablespoons low fat plain yogurt
a bunch of spring onions, chopped finely
1 teaspoon ground coriander
4 eggs, separated
1 tablespoon kalonji seeds (optional)
salt and freshly ground black pepper

- Boil the sweet potatoes until tender and then drain.
- Preheat the oven to Gas Mark 6/200°C/fan oven 180°C. Line a 33 x 25 cm (13 x 10 inch) Swiss roll tin with baking parchment and spray with low fat cooking spray.
- In a small bowl mix together the soft cheese, yogurt and spring onions and set aside.
- Place the cooked sweet potatoes in a food processor with the coriander and blend until smooth; then pulse to mix in the egg yolks and seasoning. Remove to a bowl.
- Whisk the egg whites until stiff and then stir a large spoonful into the sweet potato mixture before folding in the rest with a large metal spoon.
- Pour the mixture into the tin, tipping it to get the mixture into the corners and smoothing the top with a palette knife.
- Bake for 10–15 minutes. Meanwhile lay a large sheet of baking parchment on the work surface on a clean tea towel. Sprinkle over the kalonji seeds, if using.
- When the roulade is cooked, tip it on to the baking parchment and then roll it up and leave to cool. When cool gently unroll, spread with the cheese filling and roll up again. Cut into slices to serve.

Top tip
Kalonji or nigella seeds have a slightly peppery flavour. You can find them in Asian stores.

Mussels with tarragon

8½ POINTS values per recipe — Serves 4

185 calories per serving

Takes 20 minutes

low fat cooking spray
4 large shallots, chopped finely
2 garlic cloves, chopped finely
2 kg (4 lb 8 oz) live mussels, cleaned (discard any that are open and won't close when lightly tapped)
300 ml (½ pint) vegetable stock
a small bunch of fresh tarragon, tough stalks removed and leaves chopped
salt and freshly ground black pepper

- Spray a large saucepan with the low fat cooking spray and fry the shallots and garlic until softened, adding a little water, if necessary, to stop them sticking.
- Add the mussels and stock and cover the pan. Cook over a high heat for 3–4 minutes, or until all the mussels have opened, shaking the pan every now and then. Discard any mussels that have remained shut during cooking.
- Lift the mussels out of the cooking liquid with a slotted spoon and divide them amongst four serving bowls.
- Strain the cooking liquid into a small pan and add the tarragon. Boil for a few minutes until reduced a little, check the seasoning and then pour over the mussels to serve.

Mediterranean cod

2 POINTS VALUE

7½ *POINTS* values per recipe   Serves 4

225 calories per serving

Takes 10 minutes to prepare, 30–40 minutes to cook

Baked in the oven, this dish is quick and simple to make. Yet its robust flavours and beautiful colours make it impressive enough to serve to guests. It's good served with minted new potatoes.

2 x 400 g cans of artichokes, drained and rinsed
1 kg (2 lb 4 oz) courgettes, halved lengthways and cut into
    thick pieces
400 g (14 oz) cherry or baby plum tomatoes, halved
a small bunch of fresh thyme
2 tablespoons capers, drained and rinsed
low fat cooking spray
4 x 150 g (5½ oz) cod fillets
juice and zest of 1 lemon
100 ml (3½ fl oz) vegetable stock
a small bunch of flatleaf parsley, chopped
salt and freshly ground black pepper

- Preheat the oven to Gas Mark 7/220°C/fan oven 200°C. Toss together the artichokes, courgettes, tomatoes, thyme and capers in a large ovenproof dish or roasting tray. Season and spray with the low fat cooking spray.
- Roast for 15 minutes, until the vegetables begin to brown at the edges. Lay the cod fillets on top of the vegetable mixture and pour over the lemon juice and vegetable stock and scatter with the lemon zest. Roast for a further 15–20 minutes, or until the cod is just cooked through.
- Remove from the oven and scatter with the parsley to serve.

Tandoori chicken with minty mango raita

3½ POINTS VALUE

13 *POINTS* values per recipe   Serves 4

235 calories per serving

Takes 30 minutes plus marinating

This tandoori is not the lurid pink you may be used to. That's because it doesn't have any chemical colourants in it and, consequently, is much better for you!

2 garlic cloves, crushed
2.5 cm (1 inch) piece of fresh root ginger, grated finely
2 teaspoons ground turmeric
2 teaspoons garam masala
2 teaspoons coriander seeds, crushed
250 g (9 oz) low fat plain yogurt
juice of half a lemon
400 g (14 oz) skinless, boneless chicken breast fillets, cut into
    thick strips
For the minty mango raita
1 large mango, cut into small cubes
½ small onion, grated
½ cucumber, diced finely
1 teaspoon brown mustard seeds
a small bunch of mint, chopped finely
250 g (9 oz) low fat plain yogurt
lime wedges, to serve (optional)

- Mix the garlic, ginger, spices, yogurt and lemon juice in a freezer bag. Add the chicken and toss until covered. Seal the bag and chill for at least 30 minutes, or up to overnight.
- Meanwhile make the raita by mixing together all the ingredients and chilling.
- Preheat the oven to Gas Mark 7/220°C/fan oven 200°C. Remove the chicken from the freezer bag and place in a roasting tray. Roast for 20 minutes, until cooked through and browned on the edges.
- Serve with the raita and, if you like, lime wedges.

(1) Crab with courgette 'linguini'

2 *POINTS* values per recipe   Serves 2

100 calories per serving

Takes 30 minutes

This fresh and vibrant dish will satisfy your tastebuds and your appetite. This works well hot or cold – as a starter or main course. Try using the courgette linguini instead of the pasta in other pasta dishes too.

low fat cooking spray
2 garlic cloves, crushed
1 red chilli, de-seeded and chopped finely
zest and juice of 1 lemon
400 g (14 oz) courgettes, sliced into ribbons
170 g can of cooked white crabmeat or fresh white crabmeat
a small bunch of coriander or parsley, chopped
salt and freshly ground black pepper

● Heat a large non stick frying pan and spray with the low fat cooking spray. Fry the garlic for 1–2 minutes, until just golden.
● Add the chilli, lemon zest and courgettes and stir fry for 3–4 minutes, until just softened. Gently fold in the crabmeat, lemon juice, fresh coriander or parsley and seasoning, and then serve.

(1½) Tiger prawn curry

6 *POINTS* values per recipe   Serves 4

155 calories per serving

Takes 45 minutes

The curry paste used in this recipe could also be used with chicken, turkey or other fish. This is good served with the Aubergine crisps on page 48.

low fat cooking spray
1 teaspoon black mustard seeds
400 g can of chopped tomatoes
500 g (1 lb 2 oz) raw tiger prawns, peeled
100 g (3½ oz) low fat plain yogurt
a small bunch of coriander
salt and freshly ground black pepper
For the curry paste
1 onion, chopped
3 garlic cloves, crushed
2 red or green chillies, de-seeded and chopped
2 cm (¾ inch) piece of fresh root ginger, chopped roughly
4 teaspoons paprika
1 teaspoon garam masala
1 teaspoon ground coriander
½ teaspoon ground turmeric
½ teaspoon salt
juice of half a lemon

● First make the curry paste by placing all the ingredients in a food processor with 1 tablespoon of water and blend until smooth.
● Heat a large frying pan and spray with the low fat cooking spray, and then fry the mustard seeds. When they begin to pop add the homemade curry paste and fry for 4–5 minutes. Add 250 ml (9 fl oz) water and stir in.
● Stir in the tomatoes and cook for a further 5 minutes. Add the prawns and simmer gently for 3–4 minutes, until the prawns are just firm and pink. Check the seasoning and remove from the heat.
● When cooled a little, gently fold in the yogurt and the coriander and serve.

Chargrilled steak with roasted vegetables

(3½ POINTS VALUE) ✓

13½ *POINTS* values per recipe   Serves 4

305 calories per serving

Takes 50 minutes

This meal has an appetising range of colours, textures and flavours.

900 g (2 lb) butternut squash, peeled, de-seeded and cut
   into chunks
10 small shallots, peeled
low fat cooking spray
a small bunch of fresh thyme, leaves removed from stems
grated zest of 1 lemon
2 garlic cloves
4 x 125 g (4½ oz) sirloin steaks
150 g (5½ oz) virtually fat free fromage frais
2 teaspoons horseradish sauce
a small bunch of fresh parsley, chopped
100 g (3½ oz) baby spinach
salt and freshly ground black pepper
balsamic vinegar, to drizzle (optional)

● Preheat the oven to Gas Mark 7/220°C/fan oven 200°C. Put the squash in a roasting tin with the shallots, season and spray with the low fat cooking spray. Roast for 45 minutes, until golden and tender.

● Meanwhile put the thyme, lemon zest, garlic and seasoning in a mortar and grind with the pestle to make a smooth paste. Smooth this over the steaks and set aside.

● Mix together the fromage frais, horseradish and parsley with some seasoning and set aside.

● About 10 minutes before the squash is ready heat the grill. Grill the steaks for 3–5 minutes on each side, depending on how well you like them cooked.

● Toss the spinach in with the cooked squash and pile on to four plates. Place the steaks on top. Serve with a drizzle of balsamic vinegar, if you like, and the horseradish and parsley sauce.

Dreamy desserts

For those people who have a sweet tooth, one of the most daunting aspects of trying to lose weight can be the prospect of giving up the sweet treats that they love the most. When you take on a healthy lifestyle, it's important that you don't deprive yourself of the things you really enjoy – as you will be less likely to succeed. The trick is to have these things in moderation or find low fat alternatives that you enjoy just as much.

This chapter offers you healthier alternatives to high fat, creamy sweet treats, but with all the dreamy results. From apple tart and delightful crumble to white chocolate soufflé and delectable gâteau, the recipes in this chapter will offer you a wonderful array of marvellous desserts that will satisfy even the sweetest tooth.

Berry cheesecake mousse (page 186)

Raspberry charlotte

9½ *POINTS* values per recipe

265 calories per serving

Takes 20 minutes

Serves 2

Quick and easy and a great way to use up stale bread.

300 g (10½ oz) fresh raspberries
2½ tablespoons artificial sweetener
low fat cooking spray
25 g (1 oz) polyunsaturated margarine
4 slices of day old white bread, crusts removed
1 teaspoon ground cinnamon

● Put the raspberries in a small saucepan with 1 tablespoon of water and two tablespoons of sweetener. Cook over a low heat until the juices run from the fruit.

● Meanwhile spray a small baking dish or two individual ramekin dishes with low fat cooking spray. Spread the margarine on the bread. Mix the cinnamon and the remaining sweetener together then sprinkle this over the bread. Cut into triangles.

● Spoon the raspberries into the dish or ramekins and arrange the bread on top, cinnamon side up.

● Just before serving, heat the grill and grill for 5–10 minutes, or until the tops are golden brown and crisp and the fruit is bubbling up at the edges.

French apple tarts

19 *POINTS* values per recipe

160 calories per serving

Takes 15 minutes to prepare, 15 minutes to cook

Serves 6

Delicious individual little tarts that can be served hot or cold with low fat fromage frais. Great for a dinner party.

low fat cooking spray
1 x 200 g (7 oz) sheet of ready rolled puff pastry
1 teaspoon icing sugar
½ teaspoon ground cinnamon
½ teaspoon ground cloves
2 dessert apples e.g. Pink Lady, Fuji or Braeburn
juice of half a lemon

● Preheat the oven to Gas Mark 6/200°C/fan oven 180°C and spray a baking sheet with the low fat cooking spray.

● Roll the pastry out further until it is about 5 mm (¼ inch) thick and and then cut into six squares and lay them on the prepared baking sheet. Score with the tip of a sharp knife a border, about 2 cm (¾ inch) wide, around each.

● Mix the icing sugar, cinnamon and cloves in a small bowl and place in a small sieve such as a tea strainer.

● Core and slice the apples into thin slices and then toss them with the lemon juice in a bowl. Arrange the apple slices so that they overlap and cover the pastry squares leaving the border of pastry around each one.

● Dust each tart with the spice sugar and bake for 10–15 minutes, or until the pastry is golden brown and risen.

Sort your surroundings...

If you don't have a stop button when it comes to desserts, choose a recipe such as these apple tarts, where you can make individual portions. That way you can have your sweet fix, but you will be able to take control of the amount you eat.

2½ POINTS VALUE — Lemon, almond and strawberry gâteau

19 *POINTS* values per recipe   Serves 8

170 calories per serving

Takes 15 minutes to prepare, 45 minutes to bake plus cooling

A very light and lemony gâteau. Decorate with icing sugar and flower petals for a summery dinner party centrepiece.

low fat cooking spray
6 eggs
6½ tablespoons artificial sweetener
finely grated zest and juice of a lemon
60 g (2 oz) ground almonds
50 g (1¾ oz) plain flour
2 drops of almond essence
150 g (5½ oz) virtually fat free fromage frais
450 g (1 lb) strawberries, hulled and sliced
fresh mint, to decorate (optional)

● Preheat the oven to Gas Mark 4/180°C/fan oven 160°C. Spray a 20 cm (8 inch) cake tin with low fat cooking spray and line it with non stick baking parchment.

● Whisk the eggs until very pale and fluffy – this takes about 5 minutes of continuous whisking. Gently fold in 6 tablespoons of sweetener, lemon zest and juice, ground almonds, flour and almond essence.

● Pour the mixture into the tin. Bake for 45 minutes, until firm to the touch and coming away from the edges of the tin slightly.

● Leave to cool in the tin for a few minutes, when it will sink in the middle. Turn it out carefully and turn it over so that the golden top is uppermost.

● Leave it to cool for 1 hour. When cool, fold the remaining sweetener into the fromage frais and pile this on top of the cake. Top with the strawberries then decorate with fresh mint, if using.

2 POINTS VALUE — Papaya yogurt brûlée

7½ *POINTS* values per recipe   Serves 4

115 calories per serving

Takes 10 minutes

A simply delicious taste and texture combination that can be put together in minutes.

1 large ripe papaya, peeled and chopped into large pieces
juice of half a lime
500 g (1 lb 2 oz) 0% fat Greek yogurt
4 teaspoons light muscovado sugar

● Place the papaya in the base of an ovenproof dish or four individual ramekin dishes and squeeze over the lime juice.

● Top with the yogurt and then sprinkle each one with the brown sugar. Grill under a high heat for a few minutes, watching carefully, until the sugar has caramelised. Serve immediately.

Light chocolate sauce

2½ POINTS VALUE

9½ *POINTS* values per recipe

170 calories per serving

Takes 10 minutes

Serves 4

This lovely light and creamy sauce can be used hot or cold instead of custard to accompany hot or cold puddings. You could also flavour it with a few drops of almond essence instead of the vanilla and use it to accompany poached apricots or pears. You could even fold it through sliced bananas for a chocolate banana custard.

5 tablespoons cornflour
2 x 22 g sachets of instant low fat dark hot chocolate powder
1 litre (1¾ pints) skimmed milk
1 teaspoon vanilla extract

● Mix together the dry ingredients in a heavy based saucepan.
● Add the milk and vanilla and then stir well. Cook gently over a low heat until the mixture is smooth. Turn up the heat to medium and stir constantly with a slotted spatula scraping the bottom with the flat edge.
● When the sauce begins to boil and bubble, turn the heat down again and stir for a further 2 minutes. Remove from the heat but keep stirring for a few minutes more. Whilst hot, the sauce can be poured from a jug or the pan but as it cools it will thicken and needs to be spooned into serving bowls.

White chocolate soufflé

4½ POINTS VALUE

19 *POINTS* values per recipe

270 calories per serving

Takes 30 minutes to prepare, 40 minutes to cook

Serves 4

In modern ovens the temperamental soufflé is actually very easy to make. Have your audience waiting to be amazed at the splendour of this pudding. The soufflé can be prepared ahead of time up to step 3.

low fat cooking spray
3 teaspoons icing sugar, to dust
25 g (1 oz) cornflour
250 ml (9 fl oz) skimmed milk
100 g (3½ oz) white chocolate, broken into pieces
1 teaspoon vanilla extract
25 g (1 oz) caster sugar
2 egg yolks
5 egg whites

● Prepare a 1 litre (1¾ pint) soufflé dish by spraying it with the low fat cooking spray and then dusting it with a little of the icing sugar. Preheat the oven to Gas Mark 7/220°C/fan oven 200°C.
● In a small bowl, mix the cornflour to a smooth paste with a few tablespoons of the milk. Put the remainder of the milk in a saucepan with the chocolate, vanilla and sugar. Stir over a gentle heat until the chocolate and sugar have melted and dissolved.
● Pour in the cornflour paste, stirring constantly, and then bring the mixture to the boil. Boil for 1 minute, stirring vigorously all the time. Allow to cool a little and then beat in the egg yolks.
● Meanwhile whisk the egg whites until very fluffy then gently fold them into the chocolate mixture. Fill the soufflé dish and bake for 40 minutes without opening the oven door. Serve immediately with a dusting of icing sugar.

POINTS VALUE

Montezuma ice cream with marshmallows

4½ POINTS VALUE

17 *POINTS* values per recipe

175 calories per serving

Takes 10 minutes plus freezing

Serves 6

Montezuma was an Aztec king who was reported to have drunk vast quantities of a rich, dark, spiced, hot chocolate every day.

500 g (1 lb 2 oz) 0% fat Greek yogurt
50 g (1¾ oz) plain chocolate (preferably 70% cocoa solids), melted
a pinch of allspice
a pinch of ground ginger
1 tablespoon honey
2 x 22 g sachets instant low fat dark hot chocolate powder,
    each mixed to a paste with 2 tablespoons of boiling water
100 g (3½ oz) mini marshmallows

● Place all the ingredients except the marshmallows in a large bowl and blend until smooth and evenly mixed. Fold in the marshmallows and then tip the mixture into a freezer container or ice cream maker and freeze.

● If not using an ice cream maker, remove the ice cream from the freezer every hour and mash with a fork to break up the ice crystals.

● Remove the ice cream from the freezer 30 minutes before you want to serve it, to allow it to soften.

Fridge laundry...

If you enjoy your chocolate hit, use high cocoa content chocolate (70% or more) in your cooking. This way you'll still get the same strong chocolate taste, but you use less.

Black Forest meringue pudding

4½ *POINTS* values per recipe

90 calories per serving

Takes 25 minutes

Serves 4

This is a sweet tooth's dream of a pudding and so quick to make. It combines juice soaked bread and tart berries crowned with a cloud of meringue. Serve hot with virtually fat free fromage frais or half fat crème fraîche.

500 g bag of frozen Black Forest Fruits, defrosted if possible
8 tablespoons artificial sweetener
2 slices wholemeal bread
2 large egg whites

● Preheat the oven to Gas Mark 5/190°C/fan oven 170°C. Place the fruit and 4 tablespoons of artificial sweetener in a medium saucepan. Cover the pan and heat the fruit through.

● Meanwhile line the base of 1.2 litre (2 pint) baking dish with the sliced bread. Pour over the fruit and the juice and spread them about evenly.

● Whisk the egg whites until they are really fluffy and dry, then whisk in the remaining sweetener so that you have a thick and glossy meringue mixture. Pile on top of the fruit and spread out to cover.

● Bake in the oven for 10 minutes, or until the meringue is crisp and a pale brown colour and the fruit is bubbling up at the edges.

Rhubarb crumble

20½ *POINTS* values per recipe

225 calories per serving

Takes 35 minutes

Serves 6

This old favourite could also be made with canned rhubarb or with fresh gooseberries, apricots, plums, apples or pears. Serve hot with virtually fat free fromage frais.

1 kg (2 lb 4 oz) rhubarb, trimmed and cut into small pieces
3 tablespoons artificial sweetener
100 g (3½ oz) plain white or wholemeal flour
100 g (3½ oz) porridge oats
50 g (1¾ oz) demerara sugar
1 teaspoon ground cinnamon
50 g (1¾ oz) polyunsaturated margarine, straight from the fridge

● Preheat the oven to Gas Mark 6/200°C/fan oven 180°C. Place the rhubarb in a saucepan with 200 ml (7 fl oz) water and the sweetener. Cover and simmer for 10 minutes until soft then pour into a 1.2 litre (2 pint) ovenproof dish.

● Put the flour, oats, demerara sugar and cinnamon in a food processor. Cut the margarine into pieces and add to the dry mixture. Pulse to make a coarse blend.

● Sprinkle the crumble mixture over the rhubarb and bake for 20–30 minutes, until pale golden and the fruit bubbles up at the edges.

Food fantastic...

Oats are great for helping you to feel fuller for longer and to keep your blood sugar levels constant as oats provide slow release energy.

Chocolate rice pudding

5½ *POINTS* values per recipe   Serves 4

120 calories per serving

Takes 15 minutes

A good pud for a wintry night. This low fat comfort food can be ready in 15 minutes. It is good eaten with poached pears or apricots.

40 g (1½ oz) ground rice
2 tablespoons cocoa powder
2 tablespoons artificial sweetener
600 ml (1 pint) skimmed milk

● Place the ground rice, cocoa powder and sweetener in a small, non stick saucepan and stir together. Add a little milk and stir to a paste, then add the rest of the milk, gradually, to make a smooth blend.
● Bring to the boil and simmer for 10 minutes, stirring occasionally. Serve immediately.

Top tip

This can be made with soya or rice milk instead of cow's milk, if you prefer. You could also use two 22 g sachets of low calorie hot chocolate powder instead of the sweetener and cocoa powder. The *POINTS* values will remain the same.

Grilled apricots with marzipan

5 *POINTS* values per recipe   Serves 4

90 calories per serving

Takes 15 minutes

A very simple dessert that is a great combination of flavours and textures. You can also use canned stoned fruit or fresh plums or peaches. Serve this with half fat crème fraîche or virtually fat free fromage frais.

12 ripe apricots, halved and stoned
50 g (1¾ oz) marzipan, broken into 12 small pieces
1 teaspoon rosewater or orangeflower water

● Preheat the grill to high and place the apricots, cut side up, on a foil lined grill pan. Place a piece of marzipan in the hollow of each and sprinkle with the rosewater or orangeflower water.
● Grill for a few minutes, until the marzipan is golden and bubbling. Watch them carefully as once the marzipan starts to turn brown, it burns very quickly. Serve immediately.

Food fantastic...

Replacing dairy products such as milk or yogurt with soya is now much easier as they are widely available. This is great for people with lactose intolerance or on a low fat diet. Soya is also known to have many health benefits because it is low fat and contains easily digestible protein.

Rhubarb fool with crunchy oat topping

7½ POINTS values per recipe

105 calories per serving

Takes 20 minutes

Serves 4

The tart flavour of rhubarb is bought out by this lovely pink fool.

100 g (3½ oz) porridge oats

1 x 24 g sachet of raspberry sugar free jelly

450 g (1 lb) rhubarb, trimmed and chopped

200 g (7 oz) 0% fat Greek yogurt

4 tablespoons artificial sweetener

● Preheat the oven to Gas Mark 4/180°C/fan oven 160°C. Place the oats on a baking tray and bake for about 10 minutes until golden.

● Meanwhile place the jelly and 200 ml (7 fl oz) boiling water, in a medium saucepan. Bring to the boil stirring until the jelly is dissolved. Add the rhubarb and then cover and simmer for 10 minutes until the rhubarb is tender.

● Purée the rhubarb and jelly mix in a food processor then allow to cool for 15 minutes. Add the yogurt and sweetener to the food processor and then pulse to blend it all together.

● Pour into one large serving bowl or four individual glasses. Sprinkle over the oats to serve. Serve warm or leave to chill and set in the fridge.

Strawberry blintzes

15½ *POINTS* values per recipe	Serves 4
240 calories per serving	Ⓥ
Takes 20 minutes	(pancakes without the filling) ❄

This is one of those rare and satisfying recipes that can be rustled up in next to no time when, seemingly, the cupboard is bare. Blintzes are warm pancake parcels filled with a delectable mix of soft cheese and fruit.

For the pancake batter
100 g (3½ oz) plain flour
a pinch of salt
300 ml (½ pint) skimmed milk
1 egg
low fat cooking spray
For the filling
300 g (10½ oz) fresh strawberries, hulled
200 g (7 oz) low fat soft cheese
2 tablespoons icing sugar
½ teaspoon vanilla extract

● First make the pancakes. Place the flour and salt in a large bowl and make a hollow in the middle. Add the milk and egg and blend to a smooth batter with a fork or whisk.

● Spray a frying pan with the low fat cooking spray and pour in enough batter to cover the pan in a thin layer when swirled around. Cook for a few moments until the batter is set and the underside is golden. Tip out on to a plate, cooked side up.

● Repeat with the rest of the batter mixture to make around eight pancakes. Place a piece of baking parchment between each cooked pancake on the plate.

● For the filling, blend half the strawberries, the soft cheese, 1 tablespoon of the icing sugar and the vanilla extract in a food processor to make a reasonably smooth and creamy mixture. Spoon this in the centre of the cooked side of each pancake.

● Fold in the pancake over the filling: first pick up an edge and fold it over to just cover the filling. Then pick up the opposite edge and fold that over in the same way. Now you should have

an open-ended roll. Fold down the top and bottom to make a square parcel.

● Heat the frying pan again with another spray of the low fat cooking spray. Fry the blintzes, a few at a time, flipping them over with a fish slice until browned all over.

● Meanwhile purée the remaining strawberries with the remaining tablespoon of icing sugar and then strain through a sieve to remove the seeds. Drizzle this strawberry sauce over the hot pancakes to serve.

Top tip
This pancake recipe is very versatile and could be used either for Shrove Tuesday pancakes served with lemon and a sprinkling of sugar or as savoury pancakes. Any soft fruits could be used for the fillings. Try canned apricots, peaches, pears or raspberries. Remember to adjust the *POINTS* values accordingly.

Autumn fruit compôte

4½ *POINTS* values per recipe — Serves 4
80 calories per serving
Takes 20 minutes

A full flavoured, warming pudding or healthy breakfast.

2 dessert apples, cored and cut into wedges
2 pears, cored and cut into wedges
2 plums, stoned and sliced into wedges
2 apricots, stoned and sliced into wedges
1 cinnamon stick
1 star anise
2 cloves
2 teaspoons artificial sweetener

● Place all the ingredients in a medium saucepan with enough water to cover.

● Bring to the boil and then simmer for 10–15 minutes or until the fruit is soft. Leave to cool or serve warm.

 Grilled pineapple in lemongrass syrup

3 *POINTS* values per recipe — Serves 6
30 calories per serving
Takes 15 minutes

A very simple but exotically flavoured dessert. Delicious served with low fat plain yogurt or virtually fat free fromage frais.

1 pineapple, peeled and cut into rounds
1 or 2 lemongrass stalks, chopped into short lengths and beaten with a rolling pin
2 tablespoons artificial sweetener

● Grill the pineapple slices for 5 minutes on each side, until golden, then place on serving plates.

● Meanwhile, in a small saucepan, bring 300 ml (½ pint) of water to the boil with the lemongrass and sweetener in it. Simmer for 5 minutes, or until infused with lemongrass flavour.

● Strain the syrup over the pineapple and serve immediately.

Time saver ...

If you're short on time opt for pre-canned fruit pieces which saves the trouble of peeling and seeding the fruit yourself. However, if you do, look for the fruit canned in juice rather than syrup as it's a much healthier alternative.

Poached peaches in vanilla syrup

2 *POINTS* values per recipe

55 calories per serving

Takes 10 minutes

Serves 4

A simple recipe that even works wonders for under ripe or tasteless peaches or nectarines.

2 teaspoons artificial sweetener

1 vanilla pod, sliced in half lengthways

4 ripe peaches, sliced in half and stoned

● Pour 300 ml (10 fl oz) of water into a large saucepan then add the artificial sweetener and vanilla pod. Arrange the peaches cut side down in the pan and heat until boiling.

● Boil for a few minutes and then turn off the heat. Allow to cool before serving two halves of peach for each person, with some of the syrup spooned over.

Blackberry fool

6½ *POINTS* values per recipe

90 calories per serving

Takes 5 minutes

Serves 4

This beautiful, vivid purple fool is a perfect way of using all the soft, finger-staining blackberries available in the hedgerows in autumn. Try making it with other soft or canned fruit such as raspberries, strawberries or canned apricots, peaches or plums.

200 g (7 oz) fresh, ripe blackberries or 300 g (10½ oz) frozen
blackberries, defrosted

150 g (5½ oz) low fat Fruits of the Forest yogurt or low fat
soya yogurt

150 g (5½ oz) low fat soft cheese

2 teaspoons artificial sweetener

● Place all the ingredients in a food processor and blend until thick. Spoon the mixture into a serving bowl or individual glasses.

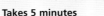

Time saver...

You can buy ready prepared frozen bags of mixed fruits in most supermarkets – which are great for a quick addition to fools and smoothies. However, if you have the time, try to use the fresh versions, as the fruit will be much juicier.

Berry puffs

½ *POINTS* value per recipe

30 calories per serving.

Takes 20 minutes to prepare, 1½ hours to cook

Makes 10–12 puffs. Serves 4

Little meringue shells encasing a sharp berry purée look great and taste divine. Serve them with bowls of fresh summer berries or orange slices sprinkled with rosewater.

low fat cooking spray
100 g (3½ oz) fresh strawberries, hulled
2 egg whites
6 tablespoons artificial sweetener

● Preheat the oven to Gas Mark ½/120°C/fan oven 100°C. Spray a baking tray with low fat cooking spray and line it with baking parchment.

● Place the strawberries in a liquidiser and blend them to a purée. Strain them through a sieve to remove the seeds.

● Whisk the egg whites until they are very dry, white and fluffy. Add the sweetener and whisk again until thoroughly mixed.

● Place dessertspoons of the meringue mixture well apart on the baking tray; make a slight hollow in the centre of each one with the back of a wet teaspoon. Place a teaspoon of the strawberry purée in each hollow and then top with a blob more of meringue.

● Bake the meringues for 1½ hours until very slightly golden and crisp on the outside. Serve them with any remaining strawberry purée.

Very cherry mousse

3½ *POINTS* values per recipe

75 calories per serving

Takes 10 minutes to prepare plus chilling

Serves 4

A simple but beautiful and delicious dessert that could be served to friends or family.

24 g sachet raspberry flavour sugar free jelly
300 g can of cherries in natural juice, drained and stoned
200 g (7 oz) 0% fat Greek yogurt
8 fresh cherries, to decorate (optional)

● Dissolve the jelly powder in 250 ml (9 fl oz) boiling water then allow to cool for 30 minutes.

● In a food processor whizz together the cherries, yogurt and jelly until smooth.

● Transfer into individual glasses and chill for approximately 2 hours, or until set.

● Serve decorated with fresh cherries, if using,

Fridge laundry...

Sugar free jelly is a great Zero POINTS value or NoCount sweet fix. Make it as a sweet end to lunch or dinner, or use it to add a lovely flavour to your desserts like in this mousse.

Berry cheesecake mousse

13½ *POINTS* values per recipe	Serves 10
95 calories per serving	(see Top tip)
Takes 30 minutes plus setting time	

This layered dessert, with a bright berry jelly on the top and a smooth and airy cheesecake mixture below, makes a very impressive dinner party dessert.

24 g sachet sugar free raspberry jelly
300 g (10½ oz) fresh or frozen summer fruits or Black Forest fruits, defrosted
2 egg whites
350 g (12 oz) low fat soft cheese
300 g (10½ oz) 0% fat Greek yogurt
zest and juice of 2 oranges
4 tablespoons artificial sweetener
3 tablespoons boiling water
1½ tablespoons gelatine powder (from a sachet or tub)

● Make up the raspberry jelly as directed on the pack and gently stir in the fruit. Pour into a 1.2 litre (2 pint) ring or other mould and chill until set. This usually takes about 3 hours.

● Whisk the egg whites until dry and fluffy. In a big bowl whisk the soft cheese and yogurt with the orange zest and juice and sweetener.

● Put the boiling water in a cup and sprinkle over the gelatine. Leave for 2 minutes and then stir it into the yogurt mixture. Beat together.

● Fold in the egg whites then spoon this mixture on to the top of the set berry mixture. Chill until the topping is set; this takes about 2 hours.

● Turn out the cheesecake mousse by dipping the mould briefly into a sink of hot water and then inverting it over a serving plate.

Top tip
This recipe is not vegetarian as it uses gelatine but you could use VegeGel instead, following the directions on the packet.

Baked apple and blackberry meringues

3½ *POINTS* values per recipe	Serves 4
95 calories per serving	Ⓥ
Takes 50 minutes	(blackberry and apple mixture) ❄

Try this fabulous pudding in autumn when blackberries are up for grabs in the hedgerows and apples are plentiful, local and cheap.

100 g (3½ oz) fresh blackberries
2 tablespoons artificial sweetener
4 cooking apples
For the meringue
2 egg whites
4 tablespoons artificial sweetener

● Preheat the oven to Gas Mark 4/180°C/fan oven 160°C. In a small bowl mix the blackberries with the 2 tablespoons of sweetener. Core the apples and score the skin around the tops with a sharp knife.

● Place the apples on a baking tray and spoon the blackberry mixture in the central cavities. Bake for 30 minutes.

● Meanwhile make the meringue. Whisk the egg whites until they are dry and white and then add the sweetener, half at a time – whisking between additions.

● Remove the apples from the oven, and turn the heat up to Gas Mark 6/200°C/fan oven 180°C. When cool enough to handle, strip off the top half of the apple skin and spoon some meringue on to the top of each one.

● Return to the oven for a further 5–10 minutes or until the meringue is crisp and golden.

Cakes and bakes

Sometimes you simply can't beat a slice of cake or a biscuit with that afternoon cup of tea and, just because you are watching your weight, you don't have to give up this pleasure. However, the ready made versions that you find in the shops, will more often than not, be laden with fatty ingredients, additives and preservatives that are simply bad for you and your waistline.

In this chapter, not only will you find recipes that are much healthier versions, but you will also find that they taste just as good and are more satisfying. From fabulous cookies and muffins to wonderful loafs and cakes, you will find that your home is filled with the wonderfully nostalgic smells of home baking.

Mediterranean flavoured soda bread

29½ *POINTS* values per recipe   Makes 16 slices

140 calories per serving

Takes 20 minutes to prepare, 40 minutes to bake   (same day) ❄

low fat cooking spray

300 g (10½ oz) wholemeal flour

225 g (8 oz) plain white flour

1 teaspoon salt

1 teaspoon bicarbonate of soda

400 g (14 oz) low fat plain bio yogurt

25 g (1 oz) sundried tomatoes (not in oil), soaked in boiling water
     to soften and then chopped

1 teaspoon mixed Mediterranean dried herbs or dried oregano

2 sprigs of rosemary, chopped finely

4 red peppers from a jar or can of roasted peppers, drained and
     chopped finely

● Preheat the oven to Gas Mark 8/230°C/fan oven 210°C and spray a baking sheet with the low fat cooking spray.

● Mix all the flours, salt and bicarbonate of soda together in a large bowl and then make a well in the centre.

● Add the yogurt, tomatoes, herbs and peppers into the well and gradually work into the flour with your hand. Add a little water, if necessary, to make a soft, but not sticky dough.

● Turn out the dough on to a floured surface and knead lightly to shape into a smooth round. Place on the baking sheet and flatten slightly until the round is about 5 cm (2 inches) thick.

● Mark a deep cross with a knife into the dough and then bake for 15–20 minutes. Reduce the oven temperature to Gas Mark 6/200°C/fan oven 180°C and bake for a further 20–25 minutes or until the bread sounds hollow when tapped on the base.

● Cool on a wire rack and enjoy warm or cooled.

Lemon drizzle cake

22 *POINTS* values per recipe   Serves 10

150 calories per serving

Takes 15 minutes to prepare, 45 minutes to cook   ❄

An absolutely failsafe recipe. Delicious served with virtually fat free fromage frais.

low fat cooking spray

150 g (5½ oz) tub of low fat plain yogurt

175 g (6 oz) self raising flour

a pinch of salt

½ teaspoon baking powder

8 tablespoons artificial sweetener

75 ml (3 fl oz) sunflower oil

2 egg whites

For the drizzle topping

grated zest and juice of 1 lemon

2 tablespoons artificial sweetener

● Preheat oven to Gas Mark 3/160°C/fan oven 140°C. Line a 18 cm (7 inch) cake tin with non stick baking parchment and spray it with low fat cooking spray. Mix all the ingredients, except the egg whites, for the cake together until smooth.

● Beat the egg whites until they are fluffy and fold into the cake mixture and pour into the tin. Bake for 40–45 minutes. Check if it is cooked by inserting a thin skewer into the centre. If it comes out clean then the cake is cooked.

● While the cake is cooking make the drizzle topping. Heat the lemon juice and zest in a small saucepan with the sweetener until the sweetener has dissolved.

● When the cake is ready take it out of oven, make holes with a skewer or fork all over the top and then pour the lemon juice mixture carefully over. Leave to cool before serving.

POINTS
VALUE

(2) Marmalade muffins

21½ POINTS values per recipe   Makes 10 muffins

120 calories per serving

Takes 35 minutes   (reheat to serve) ❄

These muffins are delicious for breakfast, afternoon tea or in lunch boxes.

150 g (5½ oz) self raising flour
¼ teaspoon baking powder
2 tablespoons artificial sweetener
1 egg, beaten
50 g (1¾ oz) low fat plain yogurt
juice of half a large orange
5 tablespoons reduced sugar orange jam or marmalade
50 g (1¾ oz) polyunsaturated margarine, melted

● Preheat the oven to Gas Mark 5/190°C/fan oven 170°C. Place 10 paper cases in a muffin tin. Mix the flour, baking powder and sweetener together in a large bowl.

● Beat the egg, yogurt, orange juice, jam or marmalade and melted margarine together in a smaller bowl.

● Gently stir the wet ingredients into the dry (see Top tip) and then quickly spoon into the muffin cases. Bake for 25 minutes or until the muffins are well risen and golden on top.

● Remove from the oven and allow to cool in the tin for 5 minutes before transferring to a wire rack.

Top tip

It's best to use a very light and quick hand to mix muffins – stop after a maximum of ten stirs. Lumps in the mixture do not matter, in fact they signify the lightness to come.

(3½) Spiced apple cake

30 POINTS values per recipe   Serves 9

220 calories per serving

Takes 30 minutes to prepare, 30 minutes to bake ❄

This cake has a layer of stewed apple sandwiched between a spiced, biscuit-style crust. It makes a great pudding served hot with dollops of virtually fat free fromage frais or it can be served cold as a cake for tea.

450 g (1 lb) cooking apples, peeled, cored and cubed roughly
8 tablespoons artificial sweetener
low fat cooking spray
100 g (3½ oz) polyunsaturated margarine
225 g (8 oz) plain flour
2 teaspoons mixed spice
2 teaspoons cinnamon
2 teaspoons baking powder
2 eggs, beaten

● Put the apples in a pan with 2 tablespoons of water and 1 tablespoon of the sweetener. Cover and heat gently until they break down to a mush, helping them along with a fork or potato masher.

● Spray a 23 cm (9 inch) square tin with the low fat cooking spray and preheat the oven to Gas Mark 4/180°C/fan oven 160°C.

● Rub the margarine into the flour with your fingertips until the mixture resembles fresh breadcrumbs. Now mix in the other dry ingredients, including the remaining sweetener. Stir the eggs into the mixture.

● Put slightly less than half the mixture into the bottom of the prepared tin and spread it around evenly, pushing it into the corners with the back of a spoon. Pour over the apple and then sandwich it with the remaining dough mixture, spread it gently and evenly over the top to cover.

● Bake for 30 minutes or until golden brown and firm to the touch. Allow to cool in the tin and then slice into nine squares. This cake can be kept in the tin, covered with clingfilm or foil, in the fridge up to three days.

Vanilla and apricot loaf

4 POINTS VALUE

40 *POINTS* values per recipe — Serves 10

245 calories per serving

Takes 20 minutes to prepare, 50 minutes to bake

This is a moist and delicious treat that will keep in a cake tin for up to four days or freeze for up to 3 months. You can serve it warm as a pudding with fat free fromage frais and fresh fruit.

125 ml (4 fl oz) sunflower oil

400 g can of apricots in juice, drained and chopped roughly

1 vanilla pod, split and the seeds removed with the tip of a knife
   or 1 teaspoon vanilla extract

100 g (3¹/₂ oz) low fat plain yogurt

125 g (4¹/₂ oz) caster sugar

1 egg, beaten

175 g (6 oz) self raising flour, sifted

1 teaspoon icing sugar, to dust

● Preheat the oven to Gas Mark 4/180°C/fan oven 160°C and line a 900 g (2 lb) loaf tin with non stick baking parchment.

● Put the oil, apricots, vanilla, yogurt, sugar, egg and flour in a large bowl and beat together until just smooth. Pour into the tin and bake for 45–50 minutes or until a skewer inserted in the centre comes out clean.

● Turn the loaf out on to a cooling rack and then dust with icing sugar to serve.

Storecupboard basics...

Keep a stock of flour, both self raising and plain. They often come in handy for cakes and bakes or for adding thickness to sauces.

(2) Stem ginger cake

34 *POINTS* values per recipe

Makes 16 slices

140 calories per serving

Takes 10 minutes to prepare, 1 hour to bake

A tasty, chewy textured, substantial cake that's great for picnics and lunch boxes.

low fat cooking spray
175 g (6 oz) porridge oats
175 g (6 oz) self raising flour, sifted
75 g (2¾ oz) polyunsaturated margarine, cut into pieces
4 pieces of stem ginger in syrup from a jar, drained and chopped
1 tablespoon of syrup from the ginger jar
2 tablespoons ground ginger
6 tablespoons artificial sweetener
1 egg, lightly beaten
150 ml (¼ pint) skimmed milk
grated zest and juice of 1 orange

● Preheat the oven to Gas Mark 3/160°C/fan oven 140°C. Spray a 23 cm (9 inch) round springform cake tin with low fat cooking spray and then line with baking parchment.

● Combine the oats and flour in a bowl then rub in the margarine until the mixture resembles fine breadcrumbs. Stir in the stem ginger, syrup, ground ginger, sweetener, egg, milk, orange zest and juice.

● Stir until all the ingredients have combined well and then pour into the tin. Bake for approximately 1 hour or until a skewer inserted into the centre comes out clean. Place the tin on a wire rack to cool completely before turning it out.

(½) Saffron scones

17½ *POINTS* values per recipe

Makes 26 small scones

40 calories per serving

Takes 15 minutes to prepare, 15 minutes to cook

Saffron may be expensive but you only need a tiny bit to colour and flavour these extra special scones.

low fat cooking spray
225 g (8 oz) self raising flour
¼ teaspoon salt
40 g (1½ oz) polyunsaturated margarine
150 ml (¼ pint) skimmed milk
a pinch of strands of saffron, soaked in 2 tablespoons boiling water

● Preheat the oven to Gas Mark 7/220°C/fan oven 200°C. Spray a baking tray with low fat cooking spray and then line with baking parchment.

● Sieve the flour into a large bowl and mix in the salt. Cut the margarine into small pieces and add to the bowl. Rub the flour and margarine together with your fingertips until the mixture resembles fine breadcrumbs.

● Make a well in the centre of the flour mixture. Pour in all but 2 tablespoons of the milk and the saffron and its soaking water and gradually stir into the mixture. Turn out on to a floured surface and knead very quickly and lightly to form a smooth dough.

● Press out the dough gently with the palms of your hands to about 1 cm (½ inch) thick. Using a cutter, cut rounds about 2.5 cm (1 inch) in diameter. Place on the prepared baking sheet. Press together the trimmings and repeat the rolling and cutting process until all the dough is used up.

● Brush the tops of the unbaked scones with a little milk and bake for 12–15 minutes until risen and golden. Cool on a wire rack until you are ready to eat. Serve warm.

Oat and cherry biscuits

21 *POINTS* values per recipe

Makes 12 small biscuits

80 calories per serving

Takes 20 minutes

Great little snacks that the kids will love too, especially in their lunch boxes.

50 g (1¾ oz) plain flour

½ teaspoon bicarbonate of soda

4 tablespoons artificial sweetener

100 g (3½ oz) porridge oats

50 g (1¾ oz) glace cherries, chopped

75 g (2¾ oz) polyunsaturated margarine

● Preheat the oven to Gas Mark 3/160°C/fan oven 140°C. Sift together the flour and bicarbonate of soda into a bowl and then add the sweetener, oats and cherries.

● Melt the margarine in a small saucepan over a low heat and pour this into the dry mixture. Mix together. Cover a baking sheet with baking parchment and take walnut-sized amounts of the mixture in your hands, flatten slightly to make a small biscuit, shape and place on the baking sheet. Leave a little space between each biscuit to allow them to spread in the oven.

● Bake for 10 minutes or until golden brown.

Strawberry shortcakes

24 *POINTS* values per recipe

Makes 18 shortcakes

85 calories per serving

Takes 20 minutes to prepare, 15 minutes to cook

These are traditional, scone-like, fluffy shortcakes that are best served hot but are also nice served cold for breakfast or tea.

500 g (1 lb 2 oz) strawberries, hulled and halved

2 tablespoons artificial sweetener

250 g (9 oz) self raising flour

a pinch of salt

50 g (1¾ oz) chilled polyunsaturated margarine

3 tablespoons skimmed milk, plus a little extra to glaze

150 g (5½ oz) very low fat plain yogurt

150 g (5½ oz) virtually fat free fromage frais, to serve

● Preheat the oven to Gas Mark 8/230°C/fan oven 210°C. Line a baking tray with baking parchment.

● Mix the strawberries with the sweetener and set aside.

● Mix the flour and salt together in a bowl. Cut the margarine into small, pea size pieces and stir them in with a fork.

● Add the milk and yogurt and mix quickly into a soft dough being careful not to overwork it.

● Turn out the dough on to a floured surface and pat into a circle about 5 mm (½ inch) thick. Cut out, with a biscuit cutter, circles about 5 cm (2 inches) in diameter. Pat together the trimmings and cut more shortcakes until all the dough is used up. Place the circles on the baking tray and brush the tops with milk. Bake for 15–20 minutes, until puffy and golden brown on the edges.

● Split open the shortcakes when cooled a little and serve with a spoonful of the strawberries and their syrup and some fromage frais.

Fresh blackberry muffins

24 *POINTS* values per recipe   Makes 12 muffins

130 calories per serving

Takes 15 minutes to prepare, 20 minutes to cook

Pick your own blackberries from the autumn hedgerows if you can as they have an unbeatably vibrant taste.

200 g (7 oz) plain flour

1/2 teaspoon bicarbonate of soda

2 teaspoons baking powder

6 tablespoons artificial sweetener

a pinch of salt

75 g (2³/4 oz) polyunsaturated margarine, melted

100 g (3¹/2 oz) low fat plain yogurt

100 ml (3¹/2 fl oz) skimmed milk

1 egg

200 g (7 oz) fresh blackberries

● Preheat the oven to Gas Mark 6/200°C/fan oven 180°C. Line a patty tin or muffin tray with 12 cup cake cases or muffin cases.
● Combine all the dry ingredients in a bowl. Separately beat the melted margarine, yogurt, milk and egg together in a measuring jug.
● Pour the wet ingredients into the dry and, using a light hand as it's important not to overwork the mixture, mix gently to combine.
● Stir in the blackberries, again keeping the mixing to a minimum, and then quickly spoon into the muffin or cup cake cases. Bake for 20 minutes, until risen and golden on top.
● Transfer to a wire rack and cool, or eat warm. Store in an airtight container for up to three days.

Wicked chocolate cake

21¹/2 *POINTS* values per recipe   Serves 10

110 calories per serving

Takes 20 minutes to prepare, 35 minutes to cook

A light but richly flavoured cake that will sink a little when it comes out of the oven. Delicious!

50 g (1³/4 oz) dark bitter chocolate (preferably 70% cocoa solids), broken into pieces

50 g (1³/4 oz) polyunsaturated margarine

1 tablespoon cocoa powder

3 eggs, separated

5 tablespoons artificial sweetener

75 g (2³/4 oz) self-raising flour, sifted

1 teaspoon icing sugar, to dust

● Preheat the oven to Gas Mark 3/160°C/fan oven 140°C and line a 20 cm (8 inch) cake tin with baking parchment.
● Put the chocolate into a bowl with the margarine, cocoa and 50 ml (2 fl oz) of cold water. Set over a saucepan of barely simmering water until melted. Remove from the heat and stir together.
● Whisk the egg whites until fluffy and dry. Then whisk the sweetener and yolks together until pale and creamy.
● Add the chocolate mixture to the egg yolk mix and whisk together. Fold in the flour and lastly the egg whites with a large metal spoon.
● Pour into the prepared baking tin and bake for 35 minutes until the cake is springy to the touch and a skewer inserted in the middle comes out clean. Cool in the tin for 10 minutes before turning out.
● When cool dust with the icing sugar, to serve.

(2) POINTS VALUE — Blueberry cookies

22 *POINTS* values per recipe   Makes 12 cookies

110 calories per serving

Takes 15 minutes to prepare, 15 minutes to cook   (dough only)

These gorgeous little cookies should be served in true American style with a big glass of skimmed milk. The uncooked cookie dough can be wrapped in clingfilm and frozen for up to three months.

75 g (2³/4 oz) polyunsaturated margarine
5 tablespoons artificial sweetener
1 egg, beaten
1/2 teaspoon vanilla extract
a pinch of salt
175 g (6 oz) self raising flour, sifted
grated zest of 1 lemon
150 g (5¹/2 oz) fresh blueberries

● Preheat the oven to Gas Mark 4/180°C/fan oven 160°C and line two baking sheets with baking parchment.

● Cream together the margarine and sweetener until light and fluffy and then add the egg and vanilla extract and beat again. Add the salt, flour and lemon zest and stir together until you have a smooth dough.

● Place tablespoons of the dough on to the baking sheets, spaced well apart and shape each one into a round. Press the blueberries into the top of the cookies and bake for 12–15 minutes, until golden. Cool on a wire rack.

Food fantastic...

Studies have shown that blueberries contain large amounts of antioxidants, which are useful in the fight against damaging free radicals.

(3¹/2) POINTS VALUE — Orange petticoat tails

44 *POINTS* values per recipe   Makes 12 wedges

215 calories per serving

Takes 25 minutes

These little biscuits make a good accompaniment to a cup of tea. They will keep in an airtight container for up to a week.

200 g (7 oz) polyunsaturated margarine
4 tablespoons artificial sweetener
40 g (1¹/2 oz) caster sugar
50 g (1³/4 oz) ground rice
zest of 1 large orange
200 g (7 oz) plain flour

● Preheat the oven to Gas Mark 4/180°C/fan oven 160°C and line a baking sheet with baking parchment.

● Place the margarine, sweetener, sugar, ground rice and orange zest in a large bowl and, mix with a fork until thoroughly mixed.

● Add the flour by sprinkling it over and incorporating it with your fingertips to form a dough.

● Place the dough on the baking sheet and roll or pat out the dough to a 5 mm (¼ inch) thick circle. Using a sharp knife, score lines out from a centre point (do not cut all the way through) like spokes on a wheel to make 12 small wedges. Bake for 15 minutes, until golden brown.

● To serve slice up the biscuit into the 12 wedges.

Top tip

It helps to keep the mixture cool or it may become too sticky. The mixture can be refrigerated for 10 minutes or so before rolling out if it is too difficult to handle. Ground rice is available from the baking section of most supermarkets. It cooks quickly and adds texture to these biscuits.

Courgette tea cake

26 *POINTS* values per recipe   Serves 10

190 calories per serving

Takes 20 minutes to prepare, 2 hours to bake

A lovely dense cake that tastes delicious. The courgettes have the same effect as the carrots in carrot cake – they enhance the texture and give the cake a moistness and richer flavour. This cake is made in a loaf tin and sliced like bread but it could also be made in a 20 cm (8 inch) springform, round cake tin if you prefer.

low fat cooking spray

75 g (2³⁄4 oz) polyunsaturated margarine

6 tablespoons artificial sweetener

450 g (1 lb) courgettes, grated

100 g (3¹⁄2 oz) stoned dates, chopped

100 ml (3¹⁄2 fl oz) orange juice

200 g (7 oz) self raising flour

¹⁄2 teaspoon bicarbonate of soda

¹⁄2 teaspoon salt

2 teaspoons cinnamon

¹⁄2 teaspoon ground cloves

2 eggs, beaten

● Preheat the oven to Gas Mark 4/180°C/fan oven 160°C. Spray a 1.2 litre (2 pint) loaf tin with low fat cooking spray and line it with baking parchment.

● Cream together the margarine and sweetener until pale and fluffy.

● Stir in the other ingredients. Tip into the prepared tin and bake for 30 minutes until well risen and just firm. If the top starts browning too much before the cake is cooked through, cover it with a piece of foil.

● Leave in the tin until cool and then turn out on to a serving plate and slice to serve. This cake keeps in an airtight container for up to one week.

Moist mango cake

12¹⁄2 *POINTS* values per recipe   Serves 12

80 calories per serving

Takes 20 minutes to prepare, 45 minutes to bake

An exotically flavoured light but moist cake that works well as a dessert. Serve with virtually fat free fromage frais.

low fat cooking spray

2 egg whites

1 egg, separated

8 tablespoons artificial sweetener

425 g can mango slices in juice, drained and puréed in a food processor

2 drops vanilla essence

1 tablespoon sunflower oil

125 g (4¹⁄2 oz) self raising flour

1 teaspoon icing sugar, to dust

● Preheat the oven to Gas Mark 4/180°C/fan oven 160°C and spray a 20 cm (8 inch) round spring form baking tin with low fat cooking spray.

● In a large bowl whisk the egg whites until dry and fluffy. In another large bowl mix the sweetener, egg yolk, mango purée, vanilla, oil and flour.

● Fold in the whisked egg whites and then pour into the prepared tin and bake for 45 minutes, until golden and risen and a skewer inserted in the middle comes out clean.

● Allow to cool before removing from the tin, then dust with icing sugar to serve.

Cinnamon cookies

26 POINTS values per recipe

55 calories per serving

Takes 20 minutes to prepare, 15 minutes to cook (uncooked dough) ❄

Makes 25 biscuits

Ⓥ

These light cookies can be cut into shapes such as stars, hearts and moons and used for Christmas decorations.

250 g (9 oz) self raising flour
1 tablespoon ground cinnamon
1 tablespoon ground ginger
6 tablespoons artificial sweetener
75 g (2¾ oz) polyunsaturated margarine
1 large egg white
2 tablespoons golden syrup or honey
1 tablespoon icing sugar, to dust

● Preheat the oven to Gas Mark 3/160°C/fan oven 140°C. Place the flour, cinnamon, ginger and sweetener in a large bowl and stir together. Add the margarine and rub in to the mixture with your hands until it resembles fine breadcrumbs.

● Beat the egg white and the syrup or honey together in a jug or small bowl. Make a well in the middle of the flour mixture and add the egg mix.

● Mix everything together gently, until you have a ball of soft dough. Wrap in a plastic bag or baking parchment and refrigerate for 30 minutes or so as this will help when rolling it out.

● Roll out the dough on a floured surface until about 5 mm (¼ inch) thick. Cut out approximately 25 biscuits using cutters about 5 cm (2 inches) in diameter. Line a baking tray with baking parchment.

● Place the shapes on the baking sheet and bake for 15 minutes, until golden brown. Place on a cooling rack to cool. Dust with icing sugar to serve.

Top tip
To measure tablespoons of golden syrup or honey, first dip the measuring spoon into boiling water so the syrup won't stick.

These cookies can be kept in an airtight tin for up to a week.

Index by *POINTS* values

Breakfasts and brunches

3 *POINTS* values and under
Bold berry smoothie 14
Eggs Florentine 13
Oaty pancakes with blueberries 13
Zingy vegetable juice 16

4 *POINTS* values and under
Big fruit kickstart 16
Croque monsieur 10
Full English breakfast 10
Power porridge 15
Smoked salmon and scrambled eggs 15

Scrumptious soups

1 *POINT* value and under
Asparagus and fromage frais soup 24
Courgette and coriander soup 30
Jaipur-style dahl soup 32
Roast butternut squash soup 28
Roast tomato and garlic soup 31
Thai spinach soup 20

2 *POINTS* values and under
All season minestrone 30
Leek and potato soup 31
Summer vegetable soup 23
Sweet potato and chilli soup 28

3 *POINTS* values and under
Beetroot and crème fraîche soup 23
Fabulous fish and bean soup 27
French onion soup 20

4 *POINTS* values and under
Summer pea, ham and mint soup 27

5 *POINTS* values and under
Lentil, porcini and bacon soup 32
Parsnip, ham and apple soup 24

Vibrant veggies

1 *POINTS* value and under
Aubergine crisps 48
Aubergine dip 47
Braised red cabbage 39
Courgettes with mint 46

French style braised peas and carrots 41
Green beans with rosemary 38
Leeks à la niçoise 44
Roasted roots 41
Roasted vegetables with yogurt sauce 42
Stir fried Savoy cabbage with garlic and chilli 47
Warm broccoli salad with mustard dressing 46

2 *POINTS* values and under
Celeriac mash with onion gravy 48
Roasted stuffed mushrooms 42

3 *POINTS* values and under
Spicy parsnip and leek patties 43
Veggie burger 38

4 *POINTS* values and under
Potato wedges with chilli dip 44

5 *POINTS* values and under
Mediterranean pasta salad 36

6 *POINTS* values and under
Creamy penne with peas 43
Soufflé baked potatoes 36

Food in a flash

2 *POINTS* values and under
Sesame chicken 54
Sticky marmalade turkey escalopes 58
Stir fried broccoli and tofu 63
Stir fried pork with baby sweetcorn 60

3 *POINTS* values and under
Cod parcels with lemon and dill sauce 64

4 *POINTS* values and under
Chicken noodles 68
Glazed pork chops with mushroom ragu 52
Pad Thai 58
Smoked haddock and new potatoes in mustard sauce 67

5 *POINTS* values and under
Chicken with cannellini beans and rosemary 64

Hot beef noodles 62
Turkey and mango noodle salad 67

6 *POINTS* values and under
Creamy turkey crêpes 60
Fresh pasta with creamy watercress sauce 68
Grilled trout with Chinese vegetables 57
Nasi goreng 53

7 *POINTS* values and under
Mexican rice 57
Mushroom and ham tagliatelle 63
Spicy lamb chops with fattoush 54
Sweet and sour salmon 52

One pot wonders

1 *POINTS* value and under
Jamaican black beans 72
Vegetable balti 75

2 *POINTS* values and under
Bubble and squeak 84
Italian fish stew 76
Lemon chicken and chicory 81
Lemon and mint chickpeas 78
Pot roast turkey with autumn vegetables 84
Provençal casserole 82
Sausage and bean stew 72

3 *POINTS* values and under
Sweet vegetable stew 75
Tuscan beans 78

4 *POINTS* values and under
Baked cheesey leeks 82
Chicken Kashmiri 83

5 *POINTS* values and under
Chicken and spring vegetable fricassée 83
Chicken goulash with dumplings 79
Spaghetti Napoli 76

6 *POINTS* values and under
Italian grilled chicken with sage and beans 81

Family favourites

2 *POINTS* values and under
Creamy turkey and pepper fricassée 108
Vegetable chilli 100

3 *POINTS* values and under
Easy pizzas 92
Roast pork chops with apple stuffing 109
Traditional fishcakes 104
Turkey and watercress rolls 108
Tzatziki turkey burgers 104
Vegetable risotto 103

4 *POINTS* values and under
Bangers and mash with onion gravy 89
Lasagne 96
Meatloaf 92
Moussaka 100
Nut roast with garlic and tomato sauce 88
Roast chicken with rosemary and lemon potatoes 94

5 *POINTS* values and under
Cheesey beanburgers 91
Spaghetti bolognese 103

6 *POINTS* values and under
Chicken biryani 109
Easy frying pan fish pie 99
Pork roast with ratatouille 107
Roast salmon fillets with tangy tomato crust 91

7 *POINTS* values and under
Cheesey pasta and ham bake 89
Shepherd's pie 99

9 *POINTS* values and under
Tandoori lamb with warm rice salad 107

Light lunches

1 *POINTS* value and under
Crunchy coleslaw 118
Marinated mushroom antipasto 121